Tanya ... an i...
children, inc.. .di...
Apprentice, The W... ...ton and *The Kraken Snores,* and three stories featuring the characters Flotsam and Jetsam. Of *Love Him to Death*, the eighth title in her popular murder mystery series, Tanya says, "I love celebrity weddings – the more ludicrously flamboyant, the better! I was reading about a particularly tacky one when it occurred to me that it would make a great backdrop for a murder mystery."

Tanya is also the author of two novels for teen-agers: *Apache*, which was shortlisted for the Carnegie Medal and the Booktrust Teenage Fiction Prize, and *The Goldsmith's Daughter*, which was nominated for the Guardian Children's Fiction Prize. Since 1992, Tanya has also been part of Storybox Theatre. She lives with her family in Devon.

You can find out more about Tanya Landman
and her books by visiting her website at
www.tanyalandman.com

Poppy Fields is on the case!

Mondays are Murder
Dead Funny
Dying to be Famous
The Head is Dead
The Scent of Blood
Certain Death
Poison Pen
Love Him to Death

Also by Tanya Landman

Waking Merlin
Merlin's Apprentice
The World's Bellybutton
The Kraken Snores

For younger readers

Flotsam and Jetsam
Flotsam and Jetsam and the Stormy Surprise
Flotsam and Jetsam and the Grooof

For older readers

Apache
The Goldsmith's Daughter

love him to death

tanya landman

WALKER
BOOKS

First published 2011 by Walker Books Ltd
87 Vauxhall Walk, London SE11 5HJ

2 4 6 8 10 9 7 5 3 1

This book has been typeset in Slimbach

Printed and bound in Great Britain by Clays Ltd, St Ives plc

British Library Cataloguing in Publication Data:
a catalogue record for this book is available from the British Library

ISBN 978-1-4063-2865-3

www.walker.co.uk

For Viv, who got the ball
rolling...

The puppy raised its head and sniffed the air. *Manure? Manure! Wowee! That meant cows! Ancestral memories stirred. Chase them! Bite them! Round them up!* It growled, peeling its lips back to reveal an impressive set of teeth.

"Don't be daft, Dinkum." Mick, the dog's owner, spoke sternly. The pup looked up guiltily then grinned in apology, tongue lolling out sideways.

"You're not in the Outback now, mate. Don't you start getting ideas. Heel."

The pup wagged its tail, waiting obediently by its master's side as he opened the gate into the meadow. A path led up over the hill then down to a wooded copse, where the bluebells would be just starting to bloom. Mick's heart lifted at the prospect of seeing them: he loved this time of year.

The herd had been grazing quietly by the far hedge, but when they saw the man and dog they ambled closer, propelled by bovine curiosity. By the time Mick neared the top of the hill, fifty or more cattle had surrounded him, snorting, blinking, huffing clouds of steamy breath into the morning air. He stopped to admire them.

Maybe someday he'd have a herd like this. If things

worked out, he'd get a nice place in the country. Once everything had blown over. Once Bill had seen sense... The situation was driving Angelica mad. She was already right on the edge. Suppose she totally flipped? What then? He didn't want to think about it...

Mick flapped his arms and the cattle skittered aside. He and Dinkum continued their walk. The sun crested the hill, blinding them for a moment. Neither saw the figure coming towards them, an ivory-topped walking stick raised like a club.

One well-aimed blow was all it took. Mick didn't have time to dodge or scream; he didn't have time to make any kind of noise. One minute he was standing upright, the next he was lying still, blood pouring from his head. The pup wagged its tail uncertainly. Was this a game?

The sudden violence had unsettled the herd. So when Mick's assailant began shouting and waving the stick through the air in sweeping circles, they didn't just skitter, they stampeded. And with no master's command restraining him, Dinkum did what comes naturally to an Australian cattle dog: he gave chase, snapping at their heels, driving them across the field, then back and forth, once, twice, three times, until their hooves had obliterated all evidence of the blow that had felled his master.

Mick's killer watched from the safety of the stile. A good morning's work. The police would be sure to conclude that this was the scene of a tragic accident. Natural causes. It was death by misadventure, no doubt about it.

dropping everything

My name is Poppy Fields. When we got pulled out of school for a few days and whisked off to a tiny Greek island, my friend Graham was none too pleased about what he described as "the potential long-term damage to our education". I, on the other hand, was absolutely delighted – and not just because we were missing a whole bunch of End of Term Tests and Assessments, although I have to admit that helped. No, it was because we were going to meet Bill Strummer, real-life rock star ... and witness his wedding! Right up close and personal. The world's press had worked themselves into a frenzy about it and I knew it was going to be a mind-blowingly sensational event. But little did I know quite *how* sensational…

It was July and the end of the school year was approaching fast – although nothing like fast enough as far as I was concerned. My mum, Lili, who's a landscape gardener, was away doing demonstrations at a flower show and I was staying at Graham's. His dad was at some IT conference in France so his mum, Sally, was in sole charge of us. We were sitting in their kitchen on a Sunday afternoon, and this being a typical English summer, the weather was dismal. The rain was lashing against the windows and the wind was howling around the house. We'd been doing the *"Hubble, bubble, toil and trouble"* scene from *Macbeth* at school and for homework were meant to devise a witch's spell. Graham was writing a list of ingredients but I couldn't concentrate. I was watching his mum prepare the tea with a sense of impending doom.

Sally is a freelance chef. She does all kinds of stuff: private parties, big business events, weddings, christenings, funerals. Sometimes she's really busy and sometimes she's not. This was one of the slack times and she'd taken a local butcher up on his offer of work. She was putting together a recipe leaflet for him, entitled Offally Fine, which highlighted the million and one lovely things you could do with innards and entrails – liver, kidney, heart, tongue, that kind of thing. She'd been experimenting on me and Graham since I'd arrived, and while the olive-and-kidney tartlets had proved surprisingly tasty, the tripe-and-onion trifle had been a real stomach turner. At that precise moment she was pouring raw minced liver from the food processor onto a baking tray. It looked like she'd just committed a particularly nasty murder and the tea situation was not looking good.

Then the phone rang and the world turned upside down.

Sally rubbed her hands on her apron and plucked the receiver off the wall. She hadn't even opened her mouth to say hello when a voice blasted down the line, so urgent and demanding that we could hear it right the way across the room.

"Sally? Sally, is that you?"

Sally held the phone at arm's length to avoid damaging her eardrum. "Erm… Yes, it's me. Who is this?"

"Tessa! Tessa Whittam. You remember. From college?"

"Oh, Tessa," Sally looked puzzled. "Yes, of course. I haven't spoken to you in… Gosh, how long is it?"

"Never mind that. I didn't ring for a chat," snapped the invisible Tessa. "I'm desperate. You've got to help me."

"Well … yes…" said Sally, sounding apprehensive. "I suppose so. If I can. What's the problem?"

"I'm Bill Strummer's personal assistant." Tessa paused, clearly expecting a reaction. Sally's mouth had dropped open but she didn't make a sound. Graham and I looked at each other, eyebrows raised. All thoughts of Shakespeare and spells were instantly wiped from our minds.

"You have heard of him?" asked Tessa suspiciously.

"Hasn't everybody?" squeaked Sally.

You'd need to have been living in the darkest depths of the Amazon for the last fifty years not to have heard of Bill Strummer. In fact, even that might not work: he was always doing stuff like campaigning to save the rainforests.

"Ohmigod!" Sally sighed girlishly. "I had the biggest crush on him when I was at school!"

"Well, you'll know about his wedding, then."

"Yes, of course. It's been in all the papers. Tomorrow, isn't it?"

"Yes. Twelve noon. Now look, my head chef's gone down with some hideous bug. I need someone competent over here right now, and I seem to remember you being fairly sensible. I've got all the staff and all the ingredients: I just need you to take charge. I'll email the details – you have got a laptop, I take it? I've booked you on the 19.14 to Athens. Bill's helicopter will meet you when you arrive. I'll send a car to collect you now."

"But I've got Graham…" protested Sally limply.

"Who?"

"My son. And his friend Poppy is staying with us… I can't just—"

"Bring them," snapped Tessa.

"It's term time. They're at school."

"Where?"

Sally told her.

"Leave it to me, I'll sort it out."

"But…" Sally insisted. "I can't just drop everything."

"There's a fee involved." Tessa's voice dropped and a note of low cunning crept in. She muttered something. It was too soft for me and Graham to catch, but whatever she said, it was enough to make Sally clutch the work surface for support. First the colour drained from her face and then she flushed scarlet. "Yes, well," she said briskly, "that sounds more than generous. We'll be ready and waiting. See you in Greece."

Twenty-three minutes later a stretch limousine pulled up outside and we all piled in. Sally hadn't even had time to clean up the kitchen – we'd only just managed to dash over to my place to grab my passport and swimsuit. The last thing we saw as we left were her bloody fingerprints on the phone.

If I'd been the superstitious type, I might have taken that as a bad omen.

mr nice guy

Sun. Sea. Scandal. What more could anyone want? I was in seventh heaven by the time we reached the airport, and that was before I found out we'd be flying first class. The limousine dropped us off in departures and we stopped at the newsagent's, where I bought all the celebrity magazines I could find. I also grabbed a few tabloid newspapers, all of which had photos of Bill Strummer plastered across them.

"Background research," I told Graham in response to his sideways look. "We need to know all we can about these people."

"We're hardly likely to discover anything edifying from that kind of reading material," Graham sniffed disapprovingly as he paid for his copy of *Computing Weekly*.

We checked in without any problems and were ushered through to the first class lounge, where pleasant music poured gently from concealed speakers in an attempt to soothe nervous passengers. It completely failed to work on Sally. She sat hunched over her laptop, frantically scanning the sixteen-page email Tessa had sent, muttering under her breath, "*Nuptial Nibbles*? Blissful Beach Barbecue? What's *that* supposed to mean? For *how* many people? Oh lord, how am I going to manage that? I've only got one pair of hands."

"We can help," Graham offered.

Sally patted Graham's hand absently and continued to scan the email. "That's very kind, love…" She didn't finish her sentence.

Graham's cooking skills aren't exactly legendary. He can microwave a ready meal as well as the next person, but that's about it. When we made scones once in food technology his batch emerged from the oven as hard and black as lumps of coal. (Admittedly mine weren't any better, but I'm not the child of a chef.)

"Maybe we could chop stuff up for you," I said. "Peel cucumbers, shred lettuce, that kind of thing?" Surely even we couldn't ruin salad vegetables?

"Thanks," smiled Sally. "But Tessa did say she had

the right staff. I'm sure I'll manage. Somehow." She turned back to the laptop with an anxious frown.

Graham and I sprawled on the comfy sofas and were served Coke and crisps by flight attendants with insanely wide grins. We'd just finished our second drink when the call came to board, and five minutes later we were installed in the first-class section of the plane. Sally carried on reading Tessa's email, turning whiter and whiter by the second. Graham buried himself in his magazine and I settled down with the newspapers to find out all I could about our host.

I knew that Bill Strummer was getting pretty old but that his music was as popular as ever. My mum played his stuff almost every time we went anywhere in the car. When Sally had called her from the limo to explain about our unexpected trip, she'd let out a squeal of envious rage. The she'd said with a sigh of longing, "He doesn't want his garden doing, does he? Put in a good word for me, would you, Sal?"

Even though he was a bit wrinkly about the edges, Bill was still spectacularly handsome. But it wasn't just the hit songs and the movie-star profile that made him famous: he was the music industry's Mr Nice Guy. Despite being an absolute megastar, he'd never forgotten his poor-lad-from-the-backstreets-of-London roots. He gave loads of money to charity, was famously friendly to journalists, polite to photographers, kind to his staff and, until very recently, blissfully happily married. He'd never had kids: his wife Angelica was rumoured to be a bit of a control freak who didn't want anyone coming between her and her husband. She'd toured the world with him, cooking up deliciously exotic meals for the band and crew at his concerts and producing several cookbooks to prove it. They had been a devoted, golden couple with a relationship as rock solid as Mount Everest.

Then disaster had struck – at least for Angelica. At the beginning of June this year her well-past-fifty-massively-rich-and-famous husband had met a totally-obscure-but-young-and-pretty cocktail waitress – and dumped his wife-and-childhood-sweetheart as fast as a fresh cowpat. After a whirlwind courtship of precisely three and a half weeks, Bill Strummer had divorced Angelica and proposed to Josie Diamond. Hence the hastily-arranged-but-highly-romantic wedding on a tiny Greek island that we'd be heading for the second the plane took off.

Josie Diamond had now been written about in every gossip column going, and they all went something like this: *That girl's barely twenty if she's a day – young enough to be his daughter! An absolute nobody who'd do anything to get famous! She may look sweet and innocent, but she's got her pretty little paws on one of the biggest fortunes in showbiz! She's a heartless home-breaker. A shameless gold-digger! Bill Strummer must be having a mid-life crisis, trading his wife in for a younger model. What on earth does he think he's doing?!*

To be perfectly honest, you didn't have to look very hard to see where Josie's appeal lay. Angelica had once been pretty, but the years hadn't been kind to her. In contrast, Josie was as fresh and unspoilt as a ripe peach. She had long, dead-straight, naturally blonde hair, brilliant baby-blue eyes and a complexion my gran would have described as "English rose". There were dozens of photos in all the magazines of Josie and Bill looking adoringly at each other, and I could see that whatever nasty things people had written, they were both totally besotted. Some magazines also carried photos of Bill and Angelica before the split, and they made interesting viewing. I'm fascinated by people's behaviour and how much they can say without speaking a word. It seemed to me that Bill had lost interest in his wife long before he'd met Josie. There were several shots of Angelica smiling lovingly up at Bill, but he wasn't looking back at her – he was staring sullenly straight at the camera, his bodyguard looming just behind his right shoulder like a dark shadow.

The Bill and Josie affair (or Billosie, as the tabloids

wittily renamed the couple) had caused a media explosion. Shockwaves had vibrated through the showbiz world like a scale-nine earthquake. According to one newspaper, all the A-list-celebrity guests Bill had invited to the wedding had point blank refused to go. The only ones willing to make the journey to Greece were Z-list wannabes who hoped that some of Bill's fame would rub off on them.

I turned to *Hi!* magazine, which had an exclusive deal to cover the wedding and had devoted its entire issue to Bill and Josie's love story. As far as I could see, the Big Day was going to be a sort of cross between Barbie's Dream Wedding and *Mamma Mia!* Bill had hired a luxury cliff-top villa to accommodate their guests and the ceremony would take place in a little chapel at the top of the mountain. Then there was going to be a barbecue followed by a party on the beach with Bill singing live.

As I read through the article I discovered that Josie wasn't exactly the shy and retiring type. She'd told her friends in eye-poppingly-intimate detail the whole history of her love affair with Bill, and they, thoughtfully, had related every last morsel to the *Hi!* journalist. "Josie's loved him since she was seven years old. She used to have his poster on her wall in the children's home. She kissed it every night and dreamt about the day she'd finally get to meet him." She'd got her wish when she'd been waitressing at the awards ceremony where Bill won a gong for Lifetime Achievement. "She knew right away that he was her one and only. Her wedding will be the happiest day of her life." Their first steamy kiss had happened backstage that same night ("It was so hot, they nearly set off the smoke alarms!") and he'd written a song for her right then and there on the back of the menu. "Ain't No Escaping My Love" had gone straight to number one. And now, apparently, they were already trying for a baby. ("Bill's always wanted kids. He's dying to have his own little Strummette. Josie is desperate to be preggy!")

"Euw!" I exclaimed. "Way too much information!"

"Where?" asked Graham, closing *Computing Weekly*. Curiosity had finally got the better of him.

"Take a look at that." I handed him the magazine and picked up a newspaper, which carried the other side of the story. There weren't any interviews with Angelica herself, but plenty of her friends had talked indignantly to the reporter. The divorce settlement had been more than generous – Bill had handed over the whole of his mansion and half his fortune the day he moved out – but money wasn't everything. His ex-wife was miserable and everyone knew it. A showbiz "insider" said, "I'm frightened that she might end up hurting herself.

She's desperately unhappy." "Sources close to her", "concerned friends" and "anxious relatives" all agreed that she was devastated. "Bill was hers and she was his," said one. "He was her now-and-for-ever love," explained another. "She never wanted anyone else," declared a third.

There were snatched paparazzi shots showing Angelica in varying states of distress. Tearfully leaving her house. At the wheel of her car – streams of mascara making broad black lines down her face. The worst was of her staggering through a bluebell wood. The flowers were just starting to bloom but she was clearly oblivious to the beauty of the scene. Her hair was in disarray, her shirt was coming undone so you could see her bra and her mouth was frozen open in what was obviously a cry of distress. Everything about her screamed pure misery. There was something very badly wrong about that photo. It didn't feel right to see anyone in that state – it was like walking in on them sitting on the toilet. I closed the paper.

We still hadn't taken off. The plane was delayed – some passenger or other hadn't boarded when they were supposed to. The insanely cheerful grins had slipped off the flight attendants' faces. They'd put a call out but no one had shown up and now we'd missed our slot and the other passengers were starting to complain.

Graham began tutting and checking his watch, and Sally was jiggling fretfully. "Tessa will be furious if we get to Athens late," she grumbled. "I suppose the helicopter will wait, but I don't know how I'll manage to get everything done on time. I'll have to start at the crack of dawn as it is. Maybe this wasn't such a good idea…"

"Why can't we just take off?" I asked. "Surely it's their own fault if they can't get here on time? The rest of us managed it."

"Presumably the missing person's luggage is in the hold," replied Graham. "With the threat of global terrorism, it's not possible to embark unless every passenger who checked in a suitcase is on board. Otherwise it would be a foolproof method of planting a bomb."

"Oh," I said, wishing I hadn't asked. I wasn't a nervous traveller but the thought of being blasted out of the sky was enough to make anyone uneasy. To take my mind off it I picked up another magazine.

This article took the "Angelica's perilously close to killing herself" angle one degree further, directing the threat of violence towards someone else. A "close personal friend" described how she'd been with Angelica when Josie Diamond had appeared on TV. Angelica had hurled her mug of tea at the screen. And then yelled, loud and clear, "I'm going to wring that little tart's neck!"

Which I found extremely alarming. Because just then the missing passenger finally showed up, white-faced, stick-thin and shaking like a leaf in a storm-force wind.

There we were, about to fly off to Greece on the eve of Bill and Josie's wedding.

And the person we'd all been waiting for was Angelica Strummer.

the uninvited guest

When Angelica stepped onto the plane the cabin fell completely silent. Then people began to cough and rustle their newspapers to cover up the fact that they'd all been staring, open-mouthed.

Muttering apologies to the flight attendants, Angelica slid into a seat just across the aisle and slightly in front of us, explaining to the passenger next to her that she had a terribly upset stomach.

"She must have got caught short," I whispered to Graham.

"I suppose so," he whispered back. "If you've got to go, you've got to go. Bit embarrassing for her, though."

I glanced at Angelica. She was sitting bolt upright,

her back not quite touching the seat, arms clasped tightly across her chest as if she was literally holding herself together. Her whole face was screwed up with intense concentration and her lips were moving, as if in prayer.

"Do you think she might be scared of flying?"

"It's a common phobia," Graham replied. "And it might explain the stomach upset. When it comes to fear, I believe that kind of physical reaction isn't unusual."

I kept a close eye on Bill's ex-wife over the top of my magazine. When we'd taken off and the seatbelt lights went out, everyone in the cabin visibly relaxed, unbuckling straps and reclining seats, making themselves comfortable for the journey. Everyone but Angelica, that is. She remained in the same position, as still as a statue. Only her lips moved. I couldn't hear the words, but she was muttering something to herself, over and over again, which I thought could mean one of two things. She was either (a) really frightened about flying (in which case, why had she got on a plane in the first place?), or (b) up to something.

Once we'd reached the right altitude the cabin crew brought out a trolley and started wheeling it down the aisle. When it stopped beside Angelica, the flight attendant put a hand on her arm to attract her attention. Angelica looked up and there was a flash of something desperate in her eyes that made the attendant take a step back. She refused every freebie on offer with a miniscule shake of her head, then closed her eyes again and carried on muttering, arms even more tightly wrapped around herself. It was as if she was concentrating all her energies on something important and couldn't be distracted for even one second. It was kind of spooky and reminded me of the English homework we'd been working on when Tessa's call had come through. As I watched I began to think Angelica looked less and less like a terrified traveller and more and more like a witch. Maybe she wasn't praying; maybe she was putting a curse on something. Or someone. Goosebumps popped up all over my arms.

"What on earth is she doing here?" I muttered to Graham. "Do you reckon she's going to the wedding?"

"No! Can't be…" Graham pulled a face. "It says in *Hi!* that the divorce was amicable – at least on Bill's part – but surely it can't have been *that* amicable. Can you imagine anyone wanting their ex-wife at their wedding?"

"No… It's a bit of a weird coincidence, though, isn't it? Angelica being on the same flight as us?"

"It is," said Graham thoughtfully. "And it's the kind of coincidence that's inclined to make me feel apprehensive."

"Me too."

*   *   *

Things got a whole lot more awkward when we landed in Athens. For a few minutes we lost sight of Angelica – she nipped to the Ladies as soon as we got off the plane – and then we couldn't see her in all the crush and confusion of going through passport control.

The minute we entered the arrivals lounge I noticed a huge moustached man lurking by the barrier. An impressively deep tan highlighted the contours of his razor-sharp cheekbones, and even though the sun had gone down long ago he was wearing very dark glasses. He was holding a large square of cardboard with "Sally Marshall" scrawled hastily across it in marker pen.

"Oh!" exclaimed Graham's mum, stepping towards him nervously. "That's me. Are you…?"

"Gregor Ravavich," he replied smoothly, removing his sunglasses for a moment and throwing a cheesy wink at Sally. "Come." He jerked his head towards the exit. "You are with me now."

We fell into single file, trooping obediently along behind him, but we'd barely walked three metres when we heard someone calling out his name.

"Gregor! Gregor!" The voice wasn't particularly commanding but it made him stop in his tracks. He turned. We all did. And there was Angelica Strummer, walking carefully towards us as if the linoleum floor was an ice rink.

"Holy Mother!" whispered Gregor, aghast. "What is *she* doing here?" The blood drained from his face, leaving his suntan looking like a bad paint job. Then he flushed so violently he went almost purple.

Angelica held her hands out towards him and there was nothing he could do but take them and graciously accept the air kisses she bestowed on both cheeks.

"Thanks for coming. Shall we get going?"

Gregor didn't say a thing. He just stood there, looking horrified, as Angelica linked her arm through his. She gave a small, insistent tug and we all moved off again. The super-suntanned man seemed powerless to resist. As for us – well, Angelica hadn't even glanced at Sally, let alone me or Graham. It was weird, but it didn't seem to me that she was being deliberately rude. It was more that we were invisible to her. Somehow she'd got it into her head that Gregor had come to collect her, and he was way too polite to put her straight.

I've noticed that when grown-ups are really embarrassed, they do one of two things: either they try to wriggle out of the situation or they pretend it isn't happening. Gregor had apparently decided on the second option. With a determined shrug of the shoulders that said "Not my problem" as clearly as if he'd shouted the words out loud, he allowed Angelica to come along.

Sally, on the other hand, attempted to take evasive action. Surreptitiously pulling her mobile from her bag, she tapped in a number and started whispering frantically into it. I could only hear her half of the conversation, but it went like this:

"Tessa! It's me. Sally. Sally Marshall. The *chef*! Yes. No. It was fine. Yes. Bit late but we're on our way. Listen, Angelica's here. *Angelica*... You know. Thought I should warn you."

"No idea. I haven't talked to her. But she seems to be coming with us."

"Well, Gregor's letting her. Yes, I'm sure Josie *will* go mad, but what do you expect him to do? Rugby-tackle her?"

"No, I *can't*!"

"No, I *won't*. I'm not about to start fighting a total stranger. You'll just have to deal with her when we get there."

Sally switched her phone off, huffed indignantly and then said to no one in particular, "This is going to be hideous! I'm beginning to wish I hadn't come."

"We'd have been far better off staying at home," Graham said gloomily.

I couldn't agree: this was riveting stuff!

It wasn't long before we were climbing into a helicopter. Sally, Graham and I crammed ourselves into the back while Angelica took her place in the front as if it was rightfully hers.

We took off – not a particularly pleasant experience – and soared into the night, the lights of Athens twinkling below us then gradually getting further away until they disappeared altogether and we were being carried over the empty blackness of the Mediterranean.

As we flew, Angelica's lips kept moving as they had done on the plane. And this time I was close enough to hear what she was saying, over and over, chanting in time to the whirring helicopter blades like a witch's incantation: "She has to go. I'll *make* her go. She has to go. I'll *make* her go. She has to go. I'll *make* her go."

The prospect of Josie's wedding day being the happiest of her life suddenly seemed very remote indeed.

angelica's
landing

Despite its sinister undertones, Angelica's muttering must have had a hypnotic effect on me. By the time the helicopter landed in the garden of the massive villa, I was snoring, nose pressed against the window, mouth hanging open, neck twisted at an awkward angle, Graham's elbow in my ear. When I woke up I thought for a second I must still be dreaming, because there, looking in at me with an amused smile warming his familiar features, was the man himself: the legendary Bill Strummer. He was wearing a battered denim jacket, faded jeans and a hat, which made him look more like a cowboy than a rock star. He seemed as soft and stylish as an old leather sofa: there was something about him that was instantly welcoming.

But there was nothing either soft or welcoming about the woman standing, stiffly protective, at his side. She nodded and threw a forced smile at Sally, baring her teeth like a Rottweiler about to attack. This had to be Tessa Whittam.

As Gregor released the door locks, Bill stepped forwards to help Angelica out. Gregor looked embarrassed, Tessa seemed plain angry, but Bill oozed pity from every pore. Pity and vast amounts of guilt. The poor man was riddled with it.

The sight of her ex-husband seemed to unhinge Angelica even further. For a second she shrank into herself, arms squeezing her chest again, eyes tight shut as if she didn't want to look at him. Then she took a deep breath and mumbled quickly to herself, "I'm going to put a stop to all this," before taking his outstretched hand and wrenching her face into a pathetic smile. As she stepped out I got the faintest glimpse of what she'd looked like before her husband had dumped her.

"Bill," she said croakily. "Bill."

"Good to see you, babe," he said gently. Too gently. It was like she might crumble into dust if he spoke too loudly. And then he tucked her hand carefully into the crook of his arm as if she was a fragile old lady in need of support.

Beside him, Tessa looked poised and ready to attack if Angelica did anything unexpected: her fists were clenching und unclenching as she considered where to aim her first blow.

Anyone else would have tried to hustle Angelica out of sight immediately, but this was Mr Nice Guy, remember? He looked over to where Sally, Graham and I were prising ourselves sweatily off the back seats and unfolding like crumpled balls of newspaper. He smiled, apologizing for the awkwardness of the situation with his eyes. "Hey, thanks for dropping everything, Mrs Marshall. I'm dead chuffed you could come."

"Do call me Sally," said Graham's mum as she stepped out, blushing and letting out an unexpectedly high giggle. One look at Bill and she'd transformed back into a schoolgirl with a crush.

"Hi guys," he said, turning to me and Graham – who, let me remind you, everyone had completely ignored until this point. "Sorry to drag you into this. You missing school on my account?"

"Yes," I said, adding, "a whole bunch of assessment tests. We're really gutted about it."

Bill threw back his head and guffawed. There's something nice about a grown-up who genuinely laughs at your jokes, and I couldn't help beaming back at him. That's charisma for you. The man was irresistible. Even

Graham managed one of his blink-and-you-miss-it grins.

Then Angelica shivered as if she'd been plunged into iced water.

"Hey, babe," Bill said, full of concern. "You ain't well. Let's get you into the house. We'll find you a nice room."

"With you?" She sounded desperate.

"No, babe, not with me," Bill's voice was thick with embarrassment. "You know I'm with… You know I'm getting m…" Words failed him.

"Married? You're getting married? You're going ahead with it, then?" Angelica said flatly.

"Of course."

"I see." Angelica's mouth thinned into a severe line. "I'll stop you," she declared fiercely. "I'll find a way. This won't happen. I won't allow it."

Bill was unruffled. "Look, we'll get you settled in," he said with patient concern. "Nice warm bubble bath, cup of hot chocolate. Something stronger if you need it. Then Tessa's arranged for a doctor to come and check you out."

Angelica tore her hand away from him. "I don't need a doctor!" she screamed. "I'm perfectly fine!" Then she burst into hysterical sobs and fell into a dead faint.

And so it came to pass that the first Mrs Strummer entered, in a most dramatic fashion, the luxury villa

that Bill had hired for his second wedding. We pro-
cessed along behind him as he carried his ex-wife,
swooning in his arms like the heroine of an old black-
and-white movie. He passed through the double doors
and into the entrance hall.

Josie Diamond was standing halfway up the marble
staircase, her peachy looks marred by savage jealousy.
The expression on her face announced loud and clear
that she was just about ready to commit murder.

which witch?

Josie wasn't the only person in the entrance hall. At the foot of the stairs stood an old woman who'd obviously been getting ready for bed when our helicopter landed. She was wearing a floor-length lilac nightie with matching dressing gown and fluffy slippers. When Angelica was carried in, apparently lifeless, an expression of concern creased her face. She looked very like Bill; this had to be his mother.

Concern didn't feature on anyone else's face, though. There was a whole herd of Z-list celebrities whose eyes were popping out of their heads with excitement. And a photographer – presumably from *Hi!* magazine – was happily clicking away as the drama unfolded.

Up until that point I'd been impressed by the care with which Bill had treated his ex-wife: he may have dumped her, but at least he had the decency to feel guilty about it. Then he saw Josie and everything changed.

It was as if he'd been bewitched, and I couldn't help glancing at Josie's hands to see if she was wielding a wand. The second he laid eyes on her, Bill was transformed. He literally dropped Angelica. Fortunately he'd reached a sort of floor-cushion-cum-chaise-longue arrangement in the middle of the hall, which broke her fall. As she rolled off it sideways, one unconscious hand hit the marble with an audible slap – but Bill didn't notice. He moved towards his fiancée, arms outstretched, like a man in a dream. Josie was already descending the stairs and Bill hadn't taken more than a few steps before they were face to face. He looked like he'd swallowed a vat of love potion: besotted, enraptured, hypnotized. One hundred per cent pure love was written across his features.

Josie, on the other hand, seemed brimful of hate. She glared at Bill's ex, her eyes angry little slits that burned with such furious heat I was surprised she didn't sear holes in Angelica's dress.

She turned to Bill. "What did you bring her in here for?" Her voice wobbled as if she was trying hard not to burst into tears.

Bill's smile was apologetic. "She's not well, babe," he explained. "I couldn't just abandon her. I'm sure she won't get in the way. Besides, we're solid, aren't we, you and me? We can handle this."

Bill took Josie's hand and she melted into him, her anger gone, hiding her face in his neck and blotting out the rest of the world. Shrugging helplessly, Bill looked over her head at Tessa, his eyebrows raised in a wordless plea for help.

Tessa tried none-too-gently to revive Angelica with a few slaps to the face. When that didn't work she looked around the entrance hall for inspiration. Spotting a handy vase of flowers, she grabbed it and emptied the water over Angelica. Bill's ex didn't stir and I began to wonder if the combination of shock and stress had actually killed her. But then the doctor arrived – Doctor Psychondakis, we later discovered – and he managed to revive Angelica with a shot in the arm. The moment she came round, she hurled herself at Josie, screaming, "Get away from Bill! Leave here now!"

Josie slapped Angelica across the face and there was a sharp intake of breath from all the watching Z-listers. But despite looking so frail, Angelica proved surprisingly strong when it came to unarmed combat. With a single finger jab to her stomach Angelica folded Josie in half. She then grabbed her rival by the hair, whirling her around and around like an Olympic hammer thrower. Just as Josie was in danger of being hurled through the double doors and into the night, Tessa stepped in.

If Angelica was surprisingly strong, Tessa was in a different league altogether. She came up behind Angelica and got her neck in what looked astonishingly like a Vulcan death grip. Finally, Bill's ex released his fiancée's hair and crumpled inelegantly to the floor, where Doctor Psychondakis pounced on her and shot a syringeful of tranquillizer into her other arm. Bill enfolded Josie in his arms and she began to soak his shirt with tears.

It took a few minutes for the jab to work, and in the meantime the doctor sat on Angelica's chest. She thrashed violently, trying to escape, and then her eyes fell on the old lady in the nightie.

"Ruby!" screamed Angelica. "Ruby!"

"There, there, love." Ruby walked over to Angelica and, knees audibly creaking, squatted beside her on the marble floor. I noticed that she had the same strong London accent as her son.

Angelica eyed her desperately. "*You* know. I *told* you. I said, I explained…"

"Hush!" soothed Ruby. "Calm down, sweetheart."

Tears streamed from Angelica's eyes. Her face contorted with fresh pain. "I want him back. But I can't. Never, never, never…"

Ruby's voice was gentle but firm, as if she was trying to placate a hysterical child. "You rest easy, now. You're upset, sweetheart."

"You have to talk to him," begged Angelica. "You have to stop this. You have to..." She turned her head back and forth, looking for someone in the crowd. "Where's Sizal? Sizal knows... Talk to him. Tell him he can't. He can't do this. No..."

At last the sedative kicked in and Angelica's voice became thick and confused. Her eyelids seemed to grow heavy and she blinked several times. Doctor Psychondakis climbed off her chest and helped her up. Angelica allowed him to lead her up the stairs to the room Tessa had quickly prepared earlier. She was still clutching two handfuls of Josie's hair, and the guest nearest me – who I dimly recognized from a reality TV show – muttered quietly, "Look at that! I bet Josie's got a bald patch now. Sizal Bouffant's going to have his work cut out putting that right." Then she sniggered in a not-remotely-sympathetic way.

I didn't get to ask who this Sizal person was, because once the door slammed shut behind Angelica, everyone's attention turned to Josie and Bill.

Josie looked like a toddler whose birthday balloon had burst. Her lower lip was trembling and her baby-blue eyes had filled up with tears, which were spilling over and trickling prettily over her peaches-and-cream cheeks.

"How could you let her on the island?" she asked Bill. "If she ruins our wedding, I'll... I'll... Oh, I don't know what I'll do!"

"It will be OK, babe," Bill said softly. Taking both her hands in his, he declared, "Ain't nothing going to spoil your day. I'll see to that. Tomorrow you'll make me the happiest man alive."

He sounded so sincere and so romantic that Josie smiled bravely back at him as he wiped away her tears. Then he draped his arm around her shoulder, pulling her close. Her own arm snaked around his not-as-thin-as-it-once-was waist and they walked up the stairs pressed so hard against each other, they looked as if they were in a three-legged race. They were so wrapped up in their own blissful bubble, they didn't bother saying goodnight to any of their guests – it was like the rest of us had vanished into thin air.

Tessa watched them go, and for a moment I was intrigued by the expression on her face. It was intense; penetrating; thoughtful. It reminded me of the way Snow White's wicked stepmother had looked before she'd poisoned that apple.

As soon as Bill and Josie had departed, Tessa ordered the Z-list celebrities to bed as if they were naughty children. Then she turned her attention to Ruby.

"Are you all right, Mrs Strummer? Can I get you anything?"

"No thanks, sweetheart, I'm fine. I'll turn in now. Big day tomorrow." She shook her head sadly. "How we're going to get through it with Angelica here is anyone's guess. Poor cow! Lost her marbles, she has. She'll be the death of me, that one."

"Let me worry about her," Tessa said crisply. "It's my job."

"Rather you than me, love." Ruby started to leave, but then turned back and added, "You know, any other man would have had her sectioned. Put away. But my boy's always been too kind for his own good. Soft-hearted, that's his problem." She sighed and then made her way up to bed, clearly exhausted.

By the time Ruby had gone, it was really late and Sally, Graham and I followed Tessa gratefully up the marble staircase. As we passed Angelica's door we could hear her murmuring sleepily to herself. I was pretty sure it was the same dirge-like incantation she'd intoned in the helicopter.

Tessa rolled her eyes in irritation. "As if I didn't have enough to do without having a mad woman running about the premises," she said to Sally.

Sally smiled sympathetically but was too preoccupied

with her own catering concerns to be really listening. So I took the opportunity to ask Tessa casually, "Did you work for Bill when he was married to Angelica? I mean, do you know her?"

"What was that?" Tessa looked around to see who had spoken. She was one of those grown-ups who preferred to completely ignore the existence of anyone under twenty. Eventually her eyes fell on me – looking slightly surprised, as if I was a talking cat or singing dog. "No," she replied crisply. "This is the first time I've laid eyes on her."

"So how long have you been working for Bill?" Sally asked, obviously feeling she ought to take a polite interest.

"Since June."

"What a job to land! There are people who'd kill for an opportunity like that."

Tessa laughed but it sounded slightly forced. "Don't let Bill hear you say that. I gather his last PA died rather tragically."

"Oh, really?" I asked, my curiosity well and truly aroused. "How?"

"He got trampled by a herd of cows."

Was it my imagination or just a trick of the light? Tessa's face had seemed to darken for a moment.

If Sally hadn't been there I'd have asked more, but

I could see out of the corner of my eye that she was glaring at me. Graham's mum is about as enthusiastic as mine when it comes to our uncanny talent for getting mixed up in sudden deaths. "I'm sure there was nothing suspicious about it, was there, Tessa?" she asked pointedly.

"Suspicious?" Tessa looked puzzled. "No, of course not. It was an accident. The verdict was death by misadventure, I believe."

By now we'd reached the very top of the villa, where our three tiny rooms made up what had obviously once been the servants' quarters.

"You have the best views on the island up here," Tessa told us by way of compensation. "Not that you'll have any time to admire them." She fixed Sally with a piercing stare. "You've read through my instructions, I take it? Think you can manage?"

"Oh yes," said Sally with a lot more confidence than I knew she felt. "It's all under control. I'll set my alarm for four thirty – be up bright and early to get everything done."

Tessa nodded approvingly then turned to Graham and me. "And what are you two going to do?"

"Help Mum if she needs us," said Graham. Sally looked rather alarmed at the prospect so he added, "We can lay the tables if you want."

"Hmm," grunted Tessa. "Well don't get under her feet. Things are going to be hectic enough around here without a couple of kids in the way."

She didn't wait for us to reply but turned on her heel and clicked back down the staircase without another word.

I was so tired that I crashed into bed without even bothering to brush my teeth and quickly fell into a deep sleep. But towards dawn I started to dream. I was in the audience – right in the front row – of one of those huge Roman amphitheatres, and all around me the crowd was baying for blood. Down in the ring two gladiators were fighting, but they weren't big, burly soldiers in armour. It was Josie and Angelica circling in the dust, swords pointed at each other's throats, spitting and snarling like wild animals. Beside me Bill fell to his knees begging them to stop, but they couldn't hear him over the noise of the crowd. Even if they had, I knew he was wasting his breath.

I could see in their eyes that both women intended to fight to the death.

venus and adonis

Bill and Josie's Big Day dawned as bright and sunny as you'd expect on a Greek island in the middle of summer. By the time I woke up, Sally was already hard at work. I got out of bed and pulled back the blinds to see that Tessa had been telling the truth: the view was spectacular.

The villa was perched right on the edge of a cliff – if I'd jumped out of my window, I'd have plummeted straight down into the turquoise waters of the Mediterranean. Or at least I would have done if there hadn't been a balcony jutting out from the floor below. I could see Angelica sitting on it, wrapped in a bathrobe, staring out to sea, motionless as a block of ice.

I craned my neck to the left and realized that the island consisted of two mountains rising from the sea like a pair of badly made sandcastles. We were perched on the top of one, and a chapel balanced precariously on the other. A cobbled street led from our villa down to a sandy bay, where white houses were strung out like a line of beads. Then the street climbed again, finally reaching the chapel in a series of sharp bends.

The main beach looked pretty crowded, but there was also a tiny cove nestling at the foot of the cliffs about a hundred metres away. A narrow path zigzagged down to it and there was a creaky-looking pedalo pulled up on the sand. It was a people-free zone.

We ought to check on Graham's mum first, I thought, but if she really didn't need our help, this would be the ideal place for us to Keep Out of the Grown-Ups' Way. I started rootling around for my swimming stuff, just in case. The prospect of a quiet swim seemed very appealing.

But it turned out that fate had other ideas. Suddenly there was a loud banging on my door, and before I'd even said "Come in", Tessa burst through clasping a weakly protesting Graham tightly by the shoulder. She was closely followed by a tearful Josie.

"What's going on?" I asked indignantly, uncomfortably aware that I was still in my pyjamas. "Are you OK, Graham?"

When she saw me, Tessa released Graham and crossed the floor with terrifying speed. She looked me up and down, then spun me around and made a rude remark about the size of my bottom.

"What's going on?" I repeated, looking at Graham for some clue. He shrugged, baffled, but said nothing.

"Yes," said Tessa to Josie as if I hadn't spoken, "they'll just about do. I'll get them down to Lucia right now. She'll have to do some restitching to accommodate this kid's bum, but it will be fine. Go back and relax."

Josie nodded, swallowed, took a deep breath and went back to her preparations, leaving Tessa to explain.

It seemed that the chef wasn't the only one to have gone down with a hideous bug. Overnight, two of Josie's vital bridal attendants had contracted it too. So while they were throwing up into the nearest toilet, Graham and I were being roped in to act as their replacements.

"Can't she just manage without?" Graham looked horrified. "It's Bill she's marrying, isn't it? What does she need *us* for?"

"Look," snapped Tessa, "Josie has very particular ideas about this wedding. She's been planning the whole thing since she was seven years old! The bridal attendants are integral to her whole scheme. She's worked out exactly how each photo spread in *Hi!* magazine will look." There was a pause and then Tessa added under her breath, "Bill's life won't be worth liv-ing if she doesn't get what she wants."

Now Graham might have been appalled by the pros-pect of being actively involved in the wedding, but I was thrilled. We'd have front-row seats! We'd get to witness everything. If Angelica threw a scene, we'd see every second of it. And if she didn't – well, we'd still be at the wedding of the century. It had to be more inter-esting than laying tables or shredding lettuce. It was even preferable to lying on a beach or going for a swim.

I looked at Graham. "Come on, it won't be so bad," I said cheerfully. "All we have to do is dress up a bit. We can manage that, can't we? It's not like we haven't done it before. Remember when we were flowers in *The Wizard of Oz*?"

"How could I ever forget?" said Graham bitterly. But he was weakening. I could tell.

"We'll do it," I announced.

"Thanks," Tessa replied. "I owe you one. I'll buy you some chocolate or something."

Half an hour later, when Graham and I were clad in flesh-coloured leotards and having seams adjusted and golden fig leaves stitched on in strategic places, I thought Tessa owed us more that one. In fact, she owed us about a million. And even a building-sized bar of chocolate wouldn't be enough to make up for this.

What Tessa had so carefully failed to mention was that Josie's ideas of appropriate bridal gear were either (a) refreshingly original, or (b) downright peculiar, depending on whose opinion you listened to. Sizal Bouffant, who turned out to be the hairdresser who'd been flown in for the occasion, was wildly excited about it all. ("It has the feel of ancient Rome, darling. All that excess! Quite thrilling.") Bill's mother Ruby, on the other hand, declared everything to be "blooming hideous", adding, "If she wanted a fancy-dress do, why didn't they go to Rio?"

You see, Josie was going for a Venus and Adonis theme. Graham could mutter all he liked about people who confused their Greek and Roman mythology, but Josie and Bill were dressing like a god and goddess and some of the "celebrities" were bridal attendants. There were going to be a dozen nymphs, several dryads and a lot of rather seedy-looking satyrs. Graham and I were the only children involved, and according to Tessa, our role was pivotal. We were the cavorting cupids.

We had matching pairs of white, feathery wings, tightly curled blonde wigs, and a golden bow and arrow each. Graham looked dangerously close to using his on Lucia, the dressmaker, who was currently adjusting his fig leaf.

"This is worse than the Pink Petunia," he said

through gritted teeth. "When will I ever stop listening to you? People at school will laugh themselves stupid when they see the photos."

"Maybe they won't see them," I said hopefully.

"They'll be in *Hi!* magazine!" Graham wailed. "Do you know what their circulation is? Our chances of no one spotting us are approximately forty-five thousand to one. We'll never, ever live it down."

Even I had to admit that the costumes were toe-curlingly embarrassing, but Lucia promised, "Believe me, kids, your own mothers won't recognize you when I'm through. You've got to have your make-up done yet. I'll tell Hazel to slap it on good and thick, OK? And she can stuff your cheeks with cotton wool to change the shape of your faces."

"OK." There was nothing else we could say. Because just then Tessa came striding through, snapping out instructions left, right and centre, shouting at the seam-stress who hadn't adjusted my costume quickly enough, giving my bum another withering look, and glaring at Graham and telling him he wasn't holding his shoulders straight enough and what did he think he was, a bag of chips? It was perfectly clear that, however mortifying, we had no choice whatsoever about being the cavorting cupids. Anyone who said no to Tessa might find their life expectancy severely reduced.

bouffant hair

We tested out Lucia's claim on Graham's mum. We were supposed to go straight up to have our wigs adjusted once Hazel, the make-up artist, had finished with us, but instead we slipped down to the kitchen. It was boiling hot in there, with pans simmering on every ring, and there seemed to be hundreds of people rushing in different directions. Sally was barking commands and doing something violent to half a dead animal with a very large cleaver. She did a massive double take when she saw us coming.

"What the…?"

Lucia and Hazel had clearly done a brilliant job, because she didn't have a clue who we were until

Graham mumbled through a mouthful of cotton wool, "It's me, Mum."

"Dear God!" Sally dropped the cleaver and it clattered noisily to the floor. "What on earth are you two doing?"

We explained about the bug and Tessa press-ganging us into service.

"That woman's got a nerve!" said Sally crossly. "Still, at least I won't have to worry about you getting sunburnt. Or drowned. Or both. I guess it will keep you out of trouble."

She couldn't have been more wrong.

Graham's mum was rushed off her feet, so we left her to it and took ourselves up to the room that Sizal Bouffant, hairdressing supremo, had set up as a temporary salon.

"Cupids!" he exclaimed ecstatically as we appeared in the doorway. "Darlings, how absolutely delicious you look. Straight out of Botticelli!"

"Where's Botticelli?" I whispered to Graham.

"Not where," he hissed. "*Who*. Botticelli was a painter." He didn't say any more but I could see he wasn't too thrilled by the comparison.

"Come along, my plumptious beauties!" cooed Sizal, indicating where we should sit. "By the time I've finished, you'll look truly divine."

Graham stomped across the room and dropped into his chair with a grim, tight-lipped expression. I followed, settling myself down next to him.

Sizal adjusted our wigs to fit in a matter of minutes, but it turned out that our visit to the kitchen had been a big mistake. The steamy heat had caused our ringlets to unwind and we had to spend the next hour sitting in curlers being reset.

While we were waiting, the woman who'd remarked the night before about Josie having a bald patch came in. It turned out that her name was Kelly and she was one of the attendant nymphs.

She sat down in the chair on the other side of Graham, and Sizal explained how he was going to dress her long, red hair. Apparently she didn't have any say in the matter, he was following strict instructions from Josie. He started work and it was then that I made the discovery that women like to talk to their hairdressers. I mean, *really* talk. About everything: boyfriend troubles, runaway husbands, faithless friends, money worries, holiday destinations, sick dogs and squashed cats. I reckon if you sat in a salon for long enough, you'd get to hear every single detail of a perfect stranger's life.

While Sizal plaited and twirled her hair into place, Kelly related her entire life story. It wasn't particularly gripping but it passed the time. After a while she began to ask Sizal about his work, and all of a sudden eaves-dropping got a lot more interesting. Smiling at him in the mirror, she said, "You do all the stars' hair, don't you? I bet you've got a few stories to tell."

Sizal Bouffant grinned, flashing his perfect teeth. "Oh yes, darling. I've had them all in my chair, so to speak." He winked suggestively at me and Graham. "You should see me on Oscars night. I'm doing extensions faster that Bob the Builder!"

They chatted about various celebrities, Sizal relating a whole series of hair-related titbits about which actors were going bald and who'd had a bad dye job and whose split ends were a disgrace and whether the fashion next season was going to be long or short. Then he sighed and remarked, "Of course all that's probably behind me now. If what I've read is true, I'll be dropped like a pair of hot tongs when people find out I'm doing this wedding. I may have just committed professional suicide."

I couldn't help myself. "Why?" I asked.

Sizal looked at me and pulled a face. "Angelica's friends. I don't suppose any of them will want to use me now. That's probably half my A-list clients down the plughole."

"So why did you agree to it?"

"I'm a hopeless romantic, darling. I never could resist a wedding."

Kelly didn't like being upstaged by a kid and her eyes narrowed. "You used to do *her* hair, didn't you?" she asked Sizal. "Back before Bill met Josie."

I saw Graham's back straighten and knew he was paying attention too.

"I did, sweetie. The last time I touched up her roots was January. She looked lovely then." Sizal smiled, and his expression softened as though he had fond memories. "She was radiant, you know? In love. Glowing with happiness." Then he pursed his lips and added, "Different story now, though. The poor woman seems positively suicidal."

Kelly dropped her voice. "You know she's here on the island?"

"Yes, darling. I've seen her."

"People are saying she's gone mad."

Sizal looked uncomfortable. "She does seem a little … how can I put it? *Delusional*."

"It must be embarrassing for Bill," Kelly went on. She couldn't quite disguise the tremble in her voice as she said his name. Interesting, I thought. So Kelly's got a crush on him too, has she?

"Bill?" echoed Sizal. He shrugged. "Oh, I expect he's man enough to cope. It's Angelica I feel sorry for. She's in pieces!" The hairdresser spun Kelly around in her chair and said, "You're done, sweetie." Then he added, "You know Angelica asked me to have a word with Josie?"

"With *Josie*? She never!"

"Oh yes, she did. Wanted me to stop the wedding. As if I could make any difference!"

Graham caught my eye in the mirror. We were both eager to hear more, but just then a wasp flew in through the open window and suddenly all hell broke loose.

I've never seen anyone react so hysterically to a small, stripy insect. Sizal screamed – a terror-stricken, ear-splitting squeal – then dropped his comb and started flapping his hands in front of his face in a way that only made him more likely to get stung. His breath came in wheezing gulps, as if he was about to have an asthma attack, and for a second or two I thought he might pass out in sheer fright.

But Graham – always surprisingly quick to react in an emergency – grabbed a glass and cupped it over the wasp the moment it settled. Sliding his ever-useful library card between glass and wall so he had the intruder trapped, Graham then carried the insect across the room and released it before pulling the window tight shut.

Sizal sank down on to a chaise longue, hand on heart trying to soothe its rapid beat, "Thank you," he muttered faintly. "Darlings, I'm sorry to make such a fuss. Oh dear, dear, dear, I do hate the things." Before he could explain his extraordinary outburst, the door opened once more and this time Josie came in.

"The blushing bride!" cried Sizal, quickly leaping back to his feet. "The star of the show! Come here, come here, come here! Sit, sit, sit! It's your big day, darling, and I'm going to make you look so beautiful, the gods themselves will weep with jealousy. Now be off, all of you! I need to give Miss Diamond my complete, undivided attention."

He hastily removed our curlers, squirted hairspray over us, then ushered Graham, Kelly and me out of the room with such speed that I snagged one of my fig leaves on the key that was sticking out of the door.

Graham and I had been instructed to go down to the entrance hall next, where Tessa would be waiting. As soon as we appeared she confined us to yet another chaise longue and told us to sit, without moving a muscle, while Josie was primped and preened for the day ahead. We couldn't scratch our noses or go to the toilet for fear of wrecking our clothes or make-up. All we could do was talk to each other in whispers – and the first thing we said was, "What was all *that* about?"

the blushing
bride

By now the villa's entrance hall was bursting with chattering nymphs, giggling dryads and laughing satyrs waiting to escort the bride to the ceremony. There was no sign of Angelica but we saw Bill leave for the chapel with Ruby and the other guests. Tessa was left in charge, making notes on a clipboard and issuing orders to the attendants. She looked stressed, which was hardly surprising: you could barely hear yourself think above the buzz of excited conversation. But the second Josie appeared, everyone fell silent.

Her usual look was fresh-faced and make-up-free, and even in jeans and an old T-shirt she was stunningly pretty. By the time Sizal Bouffant, Lucia and Hazel had finished with her, she looked beautiful beyond belief. She materialized in the entrance hall like a goddess and all the bridal attendants gasped. Her face was literally glowing with joy.

Kelly, on the other hand, looked almost sick with jealousy. "You look great," she said insincerely. "Nice dress."

"Oh, thank you!" said Josie. Her voice wobbled a bit as if she was nervous. "Bill chose it. I wasn't so sure about all this, but he wanted to do something really special, you know?" She looked over to Tessa. "Are we ready?"

I nudged Graham carefully, so as not to jog his fig leaves, and hissed, "She seems happy…"

"So she should be," Graham whispered back. "She's been wishing for this since she was a child."

"Be careful what you wish for," I murmured, suddenly remembering an old saying of my gran's. "Have you ever heard that phrase?"

"For it might come true," Graham finished for me. Then he added, "But Josie doesn't seem to have any reservations about achieving her life's ambition."

We didn't have time to say more because Tessa was rounding people up in earnest now and giving out orders. Our procession to the chapel was going to be a complicated affair. Half the satyrs, nymphs and dryads would lead the way, frolicking along the cobbled street to the tune of Bill's first hit, "My One, My Only". It was being played on pan pipes and lyres to fit with the Venus and Adonis theme, so it sounded a little strange, but that didn't seem to bother Josie.

Josie was riding side-saddle on a white horse that had been cunningly fitted with a pair of wings to resemble Pegasus. Graham and I were told to caper either side of it, holding our bows and arrows high. We would be followed by the rest of the attendants, who were going to sing along to the music and perform what looked like a complicated dance sequence.

Thankfully, our own routine was fairly simple – two steps diagonally left, two steps diagonally right, twirl and bow and grin.

Once Tessa had finished shouting instructions she left to join Bill and the rest of the guests at the chapel and we were off.

We hadn't gone more than a few paces when I got a stone in my golden slipper, but I didn't dare to stop for fear of causing a mass pile-up. So my performance was more of a shuffle than a caper, but Josie was so busy smiling at all the islanders who'd turned out to watch that she either didn't notice or didn't care.

We paused and posed at various prearranged beauty spots so the *Hi!* photographer could take pictures. The whole thing might have been perfectly easy if the cobbles hadn't been so uneven and the day hadn't been so hot. As it was, the procession seemed to be taking for ever.

Just as we reached the first of many hairpin bends in the road, disaster struck. Graham's face was now gleaming with sweat and my wig was itching like mad, but that turned out to be the least of our problems because suddenly Angelica appeared from behind a large rock. She scrambled inelegantly onto it and shouted at Josie over the heads of the satyrs and dryads, "You have to stop this!"

The lyres pinged their last, the pan pipes faded like a dying breath and the dancers stopped gyrating. There was silence, apart from the sound of shuffling feet as Josie's bridal attendants jostled each other for a better view. The *Hi!* photographer looked gleeful as he snapped the confrontation from every angle.

Angelica looked a mess. Her hair was blowing wildly about her face, her eyes were glinting maniacally, the tendons in her neck were standing out stiffly. "You can't marry him. Don't you see? He wants me. *Me!*"

The sight of Angelica looking so sad and so mad might have moved someone else to pity, but not Josie. Jealousy clearly brought out the worst in her and she did just about the cruellest thing she could have done: she laughed, long and loud and dripping with derision.

Angelica visibly shrunk under the weight of it.

"Hello?" Josie said sarcastically, waving an arm over the assembled bridal attendants. "What do you think all this is in aid of? He's marrying me. *Me*. Get it?"

Angelica shook her head despairingly. "Don't you see? Why can't anyone see? He loves *me*. You have to leave, go away, go home." She was begging now, her voice desperate. It was embarrassing.

Josie shook her head but said nothing more – as if Angelica wasn't worth wasting her breath on. She smiled at her attendants, beamed at the photographer, reached down and smoothed one of Graham's stray curls, then announced, "Let's get on with it. My bride-groom's waiting."

The way was steep and the sun was now directly overhead. It was absolutely sweltering. I'd removed the stone from my slipper but even that wasn't much help. We were all exhausted when we finally reached the top. The pan pipes had become screechy and out of sync with the wearily-plucked lyres. The satyrs' tails had drooped, the dryads looked like they needed water-ing and the nymphs were scarlet-faced and dripping with sweat.

Josie, meanwhile, looked as fresh and goddess-like as she had in the villa – but then all she'd had to do was sit on a horse.

Bill's mother Ruby was standing just outside the chapel, rifling through her handbag as if she'd lost something. As we approached, she looked up at Josie and cried, "You look lovely, dear."

Josie smiled. "Aren't you going in?"

"Yes, in a second. I can't seem to find my tablets. Now where on earth are they? I know I put them in here somewhere. You go on, dear, Bill's waiting for you. I'll slip in at the back. Won't be long."

Josie didn't wait to hear more. At the mention of Bill's name her chin went up and her eyes sparkled. When the nearest satyr helped her off Pegasus, she looked as excited as a toddler on Christmas Eve who had received a personal guarantee from Santa that she'd get everything on her list and more. She nodded to the musicians and they struck up "All Time and For Ever", another of Bill's famous songs. Without another glance at her soon-to-be mother-in-law she was off, me and Graham skipping half-heartedly down the aisle behind her.

The chapel was mercifully cool and dark but it took a moment for my eyes to adjust to the gloom. I bumped into a couple of guests as I twirled, and Graham caught one man across the face with his bow, but no one seemed bothered. All eyes were on Josie as she glided like a ship in full sail towards Bill, who I have to say looked like he was wearing his mum's nightie.

I took Josie's bouquet as she joined Bill at the altar, and Graham and I melted away to our allotted places in the front row. The ceremony went smoothly. Bill was as delighted by the whole thing as Josie – when he said his vows he sounded incredulous and looked at his bride as though he couldn't believe his luck. Josie spoke clearly, never breaking eye contact with Bill, adoration rolling off her in waves and washing down the aisle until everyone was caught up in this great, romantic piece of theatre. Everyone but Tessa, that is. She seemed to have a bad case of indigestion.

When the priest pronounced Bill and Josie man and wife there was a resounding cheer inside the chapel. People were clapping and grinning and dabbing corners of eyes with tissues.

But I felt distinctly uncomfortable. I'd noticed that when Josie had uttered the words "Until death do us part" her lips had curled as if, no matter how hard she tried, she couldn't suppress a self-satisfied smirk. And at that moment a shaft of sunlight had glinted off one of her incisors.

For a second the innocent, fresh-faced Josie had looked at her husband with all the carnivorous relish of a very hungry vampire.

natural causes

Once all the formal stuff was over, the musicians struck up again and Graham and I skipped back down the aisle to open the chapel door for the happy couple. It should have been an easy enough task, but when I turned the iron handle and pushed, it wouldn't budge.

The chapel was tiny and Bill and Josie were approaching rapidly. Again I turned the handle, put my shoulder to the door and shoved. Nothing doing.

"Hurry up!" hissed Graham.

"It won't move!" I complained. "You have a go."

Graham grabbed the handle. It turned smoothly enough, but when he pushed, it was as though there was some kind of obstruction on the other side. Graham looked at me and I looked at Graham. Suddenly I had visions of Angelica barring the door. What if she was about to hurl a petrol bomb through? We'd be burned alive!

Bill and Josie were only a couple of metres away now, and Tessa was sending us one of her furious glares from the front of the chapel. If we didn't get the door open – and fast – we'd be dead meat. Hurling ourselves at it, we both pushed with all our might. It budged just a few centimetres, but it was enough to see what – or rather who – was causing the obstruction.

Through the slit we could see Bill's mother lying on the ground. Her eyes were staring unblinkingly back at us and she was strangely twisted, as though she'd been wracked by violent spasms. The contents of her handbag were strewn across the ground like she'd been searching increasingly frantically for her tablets.

And hurtling down the path – running away from the chapel as if her life depended on it – was Angelica.

For the second time in less than twenty-four hours Bill carried an unconscious woman into the villa – only this time she wasn't apparently lifeless, she was actually dead.

Ruby had succumbed to a massive heart attack. While Bill had been exchanging vows with Josie, his mother had been exchanging life for death.

According to Doctor Psychondakis, it was an unfortunate accident. The old woman had absent-mindedly left her medication in her bedroom. If she'd had her tablets with her, she'd still be alive. It was sad, but there was no one to blame: she had died of natural causes.

The doctor's verdict was passed from guest to guest within seconds. Everyone agreed that Ruby's death was a bit of a downer, but nobody seemed unduly bothered about it – after all, it wasn't like any of them had known her well. The only people who'd been remotely close to the old lady were Bill, Angelica and Josie – and even Josie hadn't known her long. Bill was now sitting, distraught, in his mother's room, keeping her corpse company. Josie was pacing up and down fretfully on the terrace. Angelica had disappeared.

Meanwhile, the Z-list celebrities laid into Sally's beautifully prepared wedding feast like a flock of seagulls. Every possible taste was catered for and every international cuisine was represented: there were tables laden with everything from roast beef and Yorkshire puddings to chicken tikka masala, sweet and sour pork, green curry and pizza. But in the blazing heat neither Graham nor I felt particularly hungry. We took a small plate each and helped ourselves to a couple of chargrilled sardines and a bit of Greek salad. Then we headed for a quiet corner where we could talk.

"Do you reckon the doctor was right?" I asked Graham quietly.

He frowned. "He's a medical practitioner. He ought to know what he's doing."

"It doesn't feel quite right, though, does it?"

"No, it doesn't."

We'd come across so many suspicious deaths lately that we'd developed a fine instinct for anything dodgy.

"I reckon someone might have stolen those tablets," I said.

"What makes you think that?"

I remembered Ruby's expression as she'd rummaged in her bag. "Well, it didn't even occur to her that she might have left them back at the villa – that's why she kept on fereting around in her bag. She *knew* she'd put them in there: maybe she even remembered doing it."

"Old people's memories can sometimes be defective," Graham pointed out. "Young people's too, for that matter."

"Yes, I know – but she wasn't exactly the daft-old-dear type, was she? She seemed pretty sharp to me. Suppose someone took them out of her handbag before she left the villa? Someone who knew she had a medical condition…"

"And that climbing up to the chapel would put a big strain on her heart," Graham added. "And if she failed to take her medication, death would be the inevitable result..."

"So it might be murder?"

Graham nodded. "I agree, the whole thing does seem suspicious. Although I can't begin to imagine who would want an old lady dead. Or why."

"Murder by 'natural' causes," I said. "Very clever. Who could have done it, though? Josie? Angelica? They must have known about the tablets."

"Both women certainly had the means and the opportunity," Graham agreed. "But what about the motive? Why would either of them want to kill Bill's mother?'

I thought back to the scene we'd witnessed when we arrived. "Angelica wanted Ruby to talk to Bill. Do you remember? Maybe she'd pinned her hopes on Bill's mum talking him out of getting married, and then when it didn't work she was angry enough to want Ruby dead. She seems pretty unbalanced. And we saw her running away – that makes her look guilty."

"Guilty –or afraid. She may have simply found the body. Most people find death somewhat unsettling."

The terrace we were standing on overlooked the villa's swimming pool. At that moment Josie came into view. She'd ditched her Greek-goddess outfit and was clad in a gold bikini and matching sandals with killer heels. She seemed to be having some difficulty walking in them, as if she wasn't used to it, and looked a bit like a kid who'd raided her mother's wardrobe. She'd clearly decided to go ahead with the planned post-wedding photo shoot despite Bill's absence, because the man from *Hi!* magazine was trotting along behind her like a faithful hound. Josie settled herself on a sun lounger and the photographer circled her, snapping from every angle. Maybe she felt obliged to carry on with it. There was probably some sort of contract. Or maybe she was just heartless.

"That's not her usual look," I said thoughtfully.

"Isn't it?" asked Graham. "Is that significant?"

"Could be. She looks kind of casual in most of the photos I've seen. Wears jeans nearly all the time. Yet that outfit's downright trashy. The question is, which image is really her?"

Graham frowned. "Are you suggesting that Josie's manner of wide-eyed innocence might be assumed?"

"Yes, perhaps it's an act. It certainly worked on Bill, didn't it? And now that she's married him, she's rich. Maybe those catty things they wrote about her in the papers were true: maybe she really is a money-grabbing little gold-digger. And suppose she had it in for Ruby for some reason?"

"But why would she? Bill's mother clearly had no control over him."

"Ruby seemed quite sympathetic to Angelica, though, didn't she? That might be enough to make Josie angry."

We weren't getting anywhere. Nothing made much sense but I couldn't shake off the gut feeling that those pills had been removed deliberately. My suspicions as to who might be responsible were evenly divided between Josie and Angelica.

"I wish we knew more about Angelica," I said, frustrated. "I mean, why has she gone so completely bonkers?" I remembered Becca, a friend of my mum's, who'd gone pretty weird after her husband had walked out on her. Mum had sat up with her night after night having long, anguished discussions around the kitchen table. Becca had been desperate, but nothing like as bad as Angelica. She hadn't *completely* fallen apart. "Do you think Angelica was always a bit loopy? Maybe she was like it when they were married. If she's always been difficult, it might explain why Bill fell for Josie. I wish I knew how to find out."

There was silence for a while as we both considered the matter. Down below us came the happy sounds of minor celebrities splashing around in the pool. I noticed that Josie didn't go in the water – she was posing by the edge but seemed reluctant to take the plunge. Perhaps she didn't want to ruin her perfectly arranged hair.

"Sizal!" I exclaimed suddenly.

"What about him?"

"He used to do Angelica's hair when she was with Bill. Women talk to their hairdressers, Graham! I bet he can tell us loads about her. Come on!"

I was off, with Graham at my heels like a *Hi!* photographer, as we ran in search of Sizal Bouffant.

He wasn't stuffing his face along with Lucia and Hazel and the rest of the make-up and costume crew. He wasn't splashing in the pool or sipping a drink on the lower terrace. We found Sizal Bouffant in the room where he had adjusted our wigs earlier that day.

And there was a large wasp banging against the glass. Banging and banging, trying to get out.

Sizal wasn't hysterically begging and pleading for someone to get rid of it. He was lying, perfectly still and perfectly silent, across the chaise longue. His face was red and swollen. Five angry bumps on his cheek and neck had come up where he'd obviously been stung.

Next to him, hanging onto his lifeless arm like a drowning woman clinging to a log, was Angelica.

a sting in
the tail

Graham and I stood in the doorway staring at the dead hairdresser and his very-obviously-demented client.

"Get Tessa," I whispered out of the corner of my mouth. "I'll stay here."

Angelica's eyes were fixed on the wasp that was still battering itself against the window. Quite what I was going to do if she switched her attention to me was anybody's guess. If she'd attacked, maybe I'd have fought back or maybe I'd have just run away. As it turned out I didn't need to do either, because at that moment somebody changed the CD that was playing outside. All of a sudden, Bill's number-one hit – the song he'd written for Josie – pulsed through the distant speakers.

When the opening notes of "Ain't No Escaping My Love" rang out, Angelica started to scream. And she didn't stop. She went on and on. I thought my eardrums were going to burst but I didn't move. Neither did Graham. We were welded to the spot by the hideous sound.

Luckily the noise had the opposite effect on Bill. The room where Ruby's body was being kept was directly overhead, so he must have heard Angelica's outburst loud and clear. About thirty seconds later he pushed past us into the room, closely followed by Tessa, his constant shadow.

Bill looked at Sizal, appalled, then turned his attention to the screaming woman. Tessa, meanwhile, felt for Sizal's non-existent pulse before pulling out her mobile to summon Doctor Psychondakis yet again.

Taking his ex-wife by the shoulders, Bill lifted her to her feet, gave her a gentle shake and said softly, "Angel? Hey, what's happening?"

Angelica clamped her mouth tight shut. Her eyes flicked open and locked onto Bill's. There was a moment's silence. Then she sighed and rested her head on his shoulder, her face against his neck, just the way Josie had done the night before. She looked terribly old and tired as she answered wearily, "Natural causes."

Bill seemed both horribly embarrassed and totally

guilt-stricken. "Say that again, babe?"

"Sizal. He's allergic. He carries an EpiPen. All his clients know that. He's supposed to inject himself if he gets stung, but guess what? He left it in his room. Stupid of him, wasn't it? And now he's died of natural causes, just like the others. Accidents. All accidents. No one can prove anything, can they?"

Bill glanced around the room, caught my eye and flushed scarlet. Angelica was digging herself into a hole and we both knew it. Give her five seconds, I thought, and she'll confess to taking the EpiPen, whatever that was. But Bill wasn't going to give her the chance.

"Hey, babe, you've had a shock. Finding him like this – it's enough to upset anyone," he soothed. "You don't know what you're saying. Come on, let's get you settled down. We'll ask the doctor to give you something. Help you sleep. You'll feel better then. Tessa will sort Sizal out." He started to lead her away but then we heard the clicking of heels tottering unsteadily down the corridor and suddenly Josie was there in the doorway.

Wearing a skimpy swimsuit on the beach or by the pool is one thing, but wearing it indoors is different. It was like seeing her standing there in her bra and pants. None of us knew quite where to look.

Josie gasped, horrified, when she caught sight of Sizal. "What happened?" Her eyes darted from the ugly red swellings on his face over to the wasp banging against the window. "Did he get stung or something? Oh my God, is he dead?"

"Yes," I said.

Angelica laughed. It was high and hard and manic. "He lost his EpiPen. Silly, silly, silly Sizal."

When Josie saw that Angelica was hanging onto Bill's hand, her face changed. "Can't we get rid of her?" she said frostily to her husband. "You don't have to be Mr Nice Guy any more, Bill. Put her on a plane back to England."

Bill looked as if there was nothing he'd like more, but he just couldn't bring himself to be so harsh. "She's ill," he sighed. "I can't just kick her out. There's no one to take care of her. She might do herself some damage."

Angelica looked at Bill. "I might," she said faintly. "Yes. That would be best, wouldn't it?"

"Oh, for God's sake!" exploded Josie. "Just go home. You wanted to stop our wedding and you failed. Look," she said, dangling her left hand – complete with shiny new ring – in front of Angelica's face. "*I'm* Mrs Strummer now. Get over it." She slapped Angelica's fingers away from Bill and put her arm around him. Bill responded instantly: one touch from Josie and he forgot everything else. He was utterly besotted, everyone could see that. Everyone but Angelica.

"No." Angelica stood to face Josie. Her voice was suddenly clear and steady. Determined. "I can't. I won't. Bill loves *me*."

The chorus of "Ain't No Escaping My Love" came thumping through the speakers outside.

"Hear that?" said Josie. "That's our song. He wrote it for me."

"Bill loves me!"

"Get real," Josie sneered dismissively. Then she turned on those killer heels and wobbled out, Bill powerless to do anything but go along with her.

Angelica sank onto the chaise longue next to Sizal. Her strength seemed to ebb away. She took his dead hand in hers and said confidentially, "She can't see it, Sizal. She doesn't know. But I do. If she doesn't do what I tell her to, she'll be next!"

beach party

When Doctor Psychondakis arrived, he confirmed
Angelica's assessment: Sizal had died of natural causes.
The fact that both he and Ruby had mislaid their life-
saving medication was an unfortunate coincidence,
something the mainland police would have to be
informed of, but nothing more. At a wedding, when
everyone has their mind on other things, he said, shrugging … well, it's not so surprising.

I watched Angelica while the doctor was talking
to Tessa and was intrigued by her reaction. Bill's ex-
wife didn't look like someone who might have just got
away with two murders. She looked exhausted. Beaten.
When Doctor Psychondakis suggested escorting her

back to her room to give her another sedative, she went with him willingly. But before she left, she spoke softly to Tessa.

"You think I don't know," she said, putting her hand gently on the PA's arm and patting it sympathetically. "I can see how you feel. But *I'm* Bill's wife. He's never loved anyone but me."

Tessa went beetroot red and a few incoherently mumbled words fell out of her mouth, but Angelica didn't stay to listen.

When she had gone, Tessa turned on us. "The woman's mad," she snapped. "She's talking utter nonsense. Don't you dare go repeating any of it."

"We don't make a habit of repeating lies and gossip, Ms Whittam," Graham said indignantly.

Tessa grunted but seemed satisfied. When her back was turned, Graham and I exchanged a swift, confused glance. We didn't say anything.

The two fresh corpses had given Tessa a whole load of extra work to do. She had to arrange for them to be removed and put into cold storage before they were eventually flown home and given decent burials, plus there would be a mountain of paperwork to get through. However, she seemed remarkably untroubled by it.

While Tessa got on with it all we went off to check on Graham's mum: we knew that if Sally heard that we'd discovered another body, she'd be beside herself with worry.

You might have thought that two people dropping dead would dampen the party spirit, but it seemed to have the reverse effect. As word of Sizal's demise got around, everyone suddenly seemed desperate to live life to the full. On our way to the kitchen, Graham and I saw some guests throwing themselves into the pool, fully clothed, while others were dancing furiously to Bill's music. They all seemed to be concentrating as hard as they possibly could on Having a Good Time. Josie had persuaded Bill to sit with her by the pool and she was feeding him grapes while Kelly watched enviously from the shadows. He still looked a bit pale but was obviously trying his best not to spoil Josie's day. He had a villa full of guests, and being the lovely man he was, he clearly felt obliged to look after them.

When we finally found Graham's mum she was up to her eyeballs in preparations for the evening party, but news of Sizal's death had still managed to reach her. "Just stay away from Josie and Angelica," she begged us. "Tessa too. They all seem to be barking mad. I wish I'd never taken on this job! Thank God we can go home tomorrow."

We were quite happy to do as Sally asked. To escape from the crowds, Graham and I decided to go down to the little beach I'd seen from my window. After changing into our swimming things we trotted down the cliff path. Our cupid costumes had been horrifically hot, so it was a big relief to wade into the cool, clear sea. We had a bit of a swim and then took the pedalo so we could have a good long talk with no danger of anyone eavesdropping.

"What's going on?" I exclaimed as we began to pedal around in a large, lazy circle.

"They were both unfortunate accidents," Graham reminded me. "You heard the doctor."

"You don't believe it, though, do you?"

"Given all that we've seen and heard, the chances of both deaths being truly accidental are on the slim side," Graham admitted.

"So what we have to figure out is who would want them both dead. And why? What about Tessa? She seems to have a bit of a thing for Bill."

"Along with my mother and yours, and about ninety-nine per cent of the world's female population," Graham reminded me. "Surely that doesn't give her a motive for murder?"

"I suppose not. She had the opportunity, though."

Graham nodded. "But how about the means?"

I considered. "I don't reckon Tessa had her hair done by Sizal – she's not the hair-extensions type, is she? So she might not have known about his allergy.

And she hasn't worked for Bill for that long – she probably didn't know about Ruby's heart condition, either. Besides, even if she's in love with Bill, why would she want to kill his mother? No, you're right. I think we can cross Tessa off the list."

We pedalled in silence for a few minutes while we considered the matter. "As far as I can see, the only thing that links Ruby and Sizal is Angelica," I said finally. "She was the one to discover both bodies. And as you're always saying, the person who 'finds' a body is often the murderer."

"Very true," Graham agreed.

"But *why* would she do it?" I was perplexed. "I mean, they seemed to feel quite sorry for her. She asked both of them to speak on her behalf."

"Yet neither managed to stop the wedding."

"OK... So maybe Angelica was really angry with them. Angry enough to arrange their 'accidents'." I tried to picture Angelica in a murderous state but couldn't quite manage it. "She doesn't seem the angry type, though, does she? She looks sad and mad, but not necessarily bad. If Josie was in her position it might be different – she seems sweet enough when Angelica's not around, then she turns into a green-eyed monster."

Graham scratched his nose. "Well, Josie heard Angelica pleading with Ruby when we first got here.

And she came in to Sizal's room soon after he'd finished setting Kelly's hair. She may have overheard what he said about Angelica asking him to have a word with her. For all we know, she was mortally offended."

"So she might have got rid of both of them. But it's ruined her big day," I objected. "Which she's been fixated on since she was a kid."

"It hasn't been totally ruined," Graham reasoned. "Think of the sensation that two deaths in a single day will have caused – it makes a much more interesting story than a feature about yet another celebrity wedding. If you're right about her little-girl-lost persona being a false one, that might explain things."

"Well, if she's secretly after fame and fortune, she's certainly found it," I said. Something else occurred to me and I stopped pedalling for a moment. The vessel wobbled and Graham frowned but I ignored him. "Why did Josie come into Sizal's room just now?"

"Angelica was screaming," Graham pointed out. "I should imagine that half the island's population heard it. Maybe Josie was curious."

"Maybe. Or maybe she wanted to check Sizal was dead. Did you notice the key was in the door?"

"So?"

"Well, it was on the inside when we went to have our wigs done this morning – I snagged my fig leaf on it, remember? But when we left just now, it was on the *outside*. So someone might have locked him in there with a wasp, knowing he'd flap around and get panicky and that the thing would sting him and finish him off. And Josie was the last person to have her hair styled..."

"True. But she had to have her make-up done afterwards in a different part of the villa. Anyone could have done it then."

"Except that no one else has a motive."

"Apart from Angelica."

The more we talked, the more puzzled we became. We decided it was Josie. Then we decided it was Angelica. Then we went back to Josie again. We were literally pedalling around in ever-decreasing circles and there was no one we could consult for an opinion. The idea of telling Bill that his bride might have killed someone was laughable. Sally was elbow-deep in preparations for the evening and Tessa – well, she wasn't exactly approachable. Plus there was something odd about the way she behaved. I didn't trust her.

It seemed like there was nothing we could do.

That evening at the beach party, Sally roasted a whole ox – it looked like something out of a Greek myth and I half expected Zeus to turn up and strike a few people down with thunderbolts. Two more of the staff had succumbed to the dreaded bug during the course of the afternoon so Graham and I finally came in useful, handing out plates and cutlery to the wedding guests and collecting up empty glasses.

Bill didn't perform live in the end – he said he wasn't feeling up to it, which was understandable. Instead, the DJ played a never-ending stream of Bill's greatest hits, from early ones such as "My One, My Only" (the song that launched him on the road to superstardom, according to Graham) and "All Time and For Ever" (the first of his hits to top the charts simultaneously in Britain and the United States) to "You Won't Never Need No One But Me" (which sold a record-breaking number of copies in the first week), "I'm Yours, You're Mine, End of Story" (fifteen weeks at number one) and last year's Christmas smash hit, "He Ain't the One for You". Then the DJ put on "Ain't No Escaping My Love" and Josie and Bill danced, arms wrapped around each other, in their own little world. When the song finished, Bill got the DJ to put it on again, and then again. After the fifth time I was pretty sick of hearing it and we were both bored by the sight of grown-ups behaving like kids who'd drunk too much fizzy pop.

When Kelly suggested a skinny dip to one of the satyrs, Sally decided the beach was no longer a Suitable

Place for Children and we were despatched to the villa. Bill's music followed us all the way back and we could still hear it when we were inside, throbbing through the walls. We climbed the stairs, passing Angelica's room. The music was loud, but not loud enough to drown out her pitiful, despairing sobs. I'd never heard anything quite so lonely. It reminded me of Mum and Becca and all those heart-to-hearts around the kitchen table. Maybe they were what had kept Becca afloat.

"It's odd," I said to Graham when we reached our rooms. "Why hasn't Angelica got a shoulder to cry on? Where are all those 'close friends' of hers that were mentioned in the papers?"

"Maybe she drove them away," replied Graham, yawning. "I gather that mental instability can have an alienating effect on people."

Perhaps he was right. There was something scary about Angelica: I could see how her deep misery would put you off. But it still felt strange. I mean, when anyone at school's upset, they're like a magnet – the first sniff of a tear and girls flock around like pigeons, cooing soothing words. So why didn't someone as famous and popular as Angelica have anyone?

As I got into bed I knew there was something I was missing. Some clue I'd overlooked. If I could just catch hold of it, everything would fall into place. But right now it was like trying to grab a bar of soap – the tighter I tried to hold on, the faster it slipped away.

killer heels

I slept fitfully – the noise of the party kept waking me up throughout the night. Then, as dawn approached, there was the banging of doors and the giggling of guests as they returned to the villa and fell into their beds. By the time the house was finally quiet, the sun was pouring through the thin curtains of my bedroom. I turned over crossly but couldn't get back to sleep.

Graham must have had the same problem, because soon afterwards there was a soft tapping on my door.

"I was just seeing if you were awake," he said as he stepped into the room. He was wearing his swimsuit and had a towel in one hand.

"Awake?" I said grouchily "Of course I'm not. I'm sleeping like a log, me."

Graham ignored the sarcasm. "Fancy a swim?"

Let me explain here and now that Graham is not what you might call a natural athlete. The fact that *he'd* woken *me* for an early-morning swim was so out of character that I realized he had Things on His Mind that He Wished to Discuss. As we couldn't talk freely in the villa, the beach was our only option.

"Give me five minutes," I said, throwing back the covers and heading for the bathroom.

As it turned out, I didn't get to hear whatever it was that Graham wanted to say. When we got down to the cove we discovered that we weren't the only ones to have woken up early. Bill was sitting on a rock, gazing out to sea, looking exhausted by the events of the past two days. We stopped dead, not wanting to disturb him, but he smiled when he saw us – that kind, friendly grin that warmed you right through.

"All right, then?" he said. "Some night, eh? Enjoy the party?"

"Erm…" I wasn't quite sure what to say and didn't want to lie.

Bill laughed. "Guess it was a bit boring for kids." He changed the subject. "Hey, I meant to say – I really appreciated you helping out like that. Them cupid costumes? They was Josie's idea. And I felt like a right freak in that frock! But you've got to laugh, haven't you? What can I do? I'm putty in her hands. She's my one and only."

Neither of us could think of a reply, so Graham and I just stared silently at our feet. It wasn't long before Bill spoke again.

"Funny old day, wasn't it? Poor mum!" A tear rolled down his cheek and he looked so sad and helpless, I wanted to wipe it away for him. "Why'd she forget them pills? She's never done that before."

"She probably had a lot on her mind," said Graham, trying to sound neutral. "That's what the doctor said, isn't it?"

I wasn't so cautious. This was the first opportunity we'd had to talk to Bill alone and I wasn't going to waste it. "We wondered if someone had taken them from her bag," I blurted out.

Bill looked at me blankly. "You mean, like, *deliberately*? But that would kill her!" His eyes widened as he took in my meaning. "Blimey!"

Graham said carefully, "Angelica wanted your mother to persuade you to call off the wedding."

Bill nodded. "Yeah, Mum said. But she knew how I feel about Josie. Ain't no escaping love. It hit me like a ten-tonne truck."

His words sounded like they could have come from one of his songs, and for some reason I found it slightly unnerving.

"Do you think Angelica might have been angry with your mum?" I asked him. "I mean, angry enough to want to hurt her?"

"Angelica?" Bill winced as if even the mention of her name made him feel deeply uncomfortable. "Well, she's always been a bit... I don't know ... unstable, I suppose you'd call it. Bit of a control freak. She doesn't like it when people don't do what she wants. You don't reckon she...?" His eyes narrowed as he looked from me to Graham and back again. "Crikey! You do. What about Sizal? You reckon that was no accident either?"

Graham and I just stared at him and Bill's mind started turning things over. We could practically hear the cogs grinding. "Angelica could have put that wasp in the room, couldn't she? She was right there with him on that sofa ... and if she killed the two of them ... *Josie!* Oh my God! She's alone!"

With that he spun round and sprinted across the sand and up the steps. We were soon hot on his heels and the three of us raced back to the villa so fast, we could have won Olympic gold.

It wasn't fast enough.

By the time we reached Bill's room, Josie was

lying dead on the bed. She'd been stabbed through the neck with one of her own killer heels. And there was Angelica, sitting beside the corpse, the blood-stained shoe in her hand, telling Josie over and over again, "I warned you. I did. I told you what would happen. Why didn't you listen?"

Bill let out a low, despairing moan and staggered towards the bed, barely in control of his limbs.

Angelica looked at him. "You shouldn't have married her," she said. "Why did you do it? Why?" She examined the shoe as if she'd never seen it before. "No... I know why." Then she suddenly threw herself at her ex-husband and demanded, "You'll visit me in prison, won't you? You'll come every day. I know you will." She stared at Bill with dark, dead eyes. And strangely, for a moment, she looked as though it was the very last thing she wanted.

mick

Angelica had been caught red-handed. And yet I had a feeling it wasn't quite as simple or straight-forward as it seemed.

Tessa swung into action the second we called her. She got Gregor Ravavich to lock the unresisting Angelica in her bedroom and stand guard by the door while she sealed off Bill and Josie's suite so no one could disturb the crime scene before the police arrived. She then made about a zillion phone calls to various authorities before frogmarching all three of us to her office, where she made sweet tea.

While the kettle boiled I noticed Tessa looking at Bill with desperate concern. There was no doubt that she'd fallen for him. Had she had a schoolgirl crush too? Or had this only happened since she'd been working for him? Did it matter?

Bill broke the awful silence when Tessa handed him his tea. He looked at his cup and said in a cracked, hoarse voice, "Sorry, Tessa. I don't fancy this. Get us a coffee, would you, babe?"

When he called her "babe" – even though he said it absent-mindedly – Tessa flushed. To cover her confusion, she said brusquely, "What did your last slave die of?"

Given that Bill's wife had just been murdered, it wasn't what you might call a well-timed remark. He flinched, glanced at me and Graham then sat, staring into space while Tessa made him a cup of instant coffee.

"Hey, thanks," he said huskily when she pressed it into his hands. "How would I manage without you?"

Bill smiled gratefully at his PA, and for a second Tessa's eyes flashed with adoration and something else. What was it? Hope? It looked suspiciously like it. Bill didn't seem to notice but I certainly did. My stomach started churning.

"We'd better go and tell Sally what's happened," I announced loudly, tugging at Graham's arm. "Come on."

Tessa watched us leave with obvious relief – she didn't seem to like kids very much. We headed off towards the kitchens, where Sally was preparing the

Post-Party Pick-Me-Up for Bill's guests – a massive fried breakfast with all the trimmings, judging by the smell of bacon wafting through the villa. The minute we were out of sight I changed direction.

"Where are we going?" asked Graham, running to keep up.

"Your mum's bedroom. Her laptop will be up there, won't it? We need to look some stuff up."

"What? Why?"

"This whole thing with Angelica – her being caught in the act after all those rows and threats – it's too obvious. What if she's been set up?"

"Set up?" echoed Graham. "Well, I suppose anything's possible... But who could be responsible for plotting something so ingenious? What would their motive be? To frame Angelica, you'd have to really hate her."

"And a jealous person *would*. A jealous person who's madly in love with Bill... Josie hated Angelica enough to kill her, didn't she? You could see it in her eyes. Only then she died first and now both of them are out of the frame. Did you see how Tessa looked at Bill just now?" I asked, forging on before he could reply. "She's besotted with him, I'm sure of it. At first I thought she must have fallen for him once she'd got the job, but what if it was before? What if she's been obsessed with him since she was a kid, like Josie was?

Graham, do you remember what your mum said to Tessa when we arrived?"

Graham answered me with a passable imitation of his mum. "What a job to land! There are people who'd kill for an opportunity like that." His eyes narrowed shrewdly. "And then Tessa mentioned that Bill's former PA had died in an accident..."

"Well, maybe he didn't! Maybe Tessa committed murder to get the job! She's not a celebrity – it was probably the only way she could get close to Bill. And then killing Josie ... framing Angelica... What a neat way to get rid of your rivals!"

"And Ruby? Sizal?" asked Graham. "How do they fit in?"

"I don't know," I sighed. "Of course, we can't prove that either of those *were* murders. The doctor might actually be right. And even if he's not, it only strengthens the case against Angelica. She's the only one who might have wanted them dead. Maybe that was a good enough reason for the murderer to do it."

We'd now reached Sally's room. She'd locked it but luckily there was a door that connected through from Graham's. Once inside, Graham wasted no time in switching on the computer.

"OK," he said grimly. "Where shall we start?"

"Bill Strummer," I said. "News items. There's got to

be something about that PA's accident."

There was so much coverage about Bill and Josie that it took ages to find anything. Some of the Z-list guests had clearly been making use of their phones – there were already pages and pages of photos of the wedding and last night's party, and it was half an hour before we managed to discover anything about Bill's old assistant. Then we found a small entry that described how a man called Mick Tucker had been tragically killed by a herd of stampeding cattle back in April of this year. He'd been employed as PA to Bill Strummer for the previous six months. Tessa had told us the truth: the coroner had recorded a verdict of death by misadventure.

"Another accident," I muttered. "Do you remember what Angelica said when we found her with Sizal? Natural causes, just like the others. She didn't just say 'like Ruby', she said *others*. Plural. Why didn't I see it then? She must know something about Mick's death. We need to talk to her right now, before she gets carted off by the police."

"She may be innocent of murder," Graham warned, "but I believe she's in a highly unstable condition. Besides, Tessa has locked her up. Gregor Ravavich is standing guard outside her door – and he's massive. We can't possibly get to her."

"Oh really?" I said. "Are you sure about that?"

I steered him out of Sally's room, through his, and across the landing to mine. I threw open my window and pointed. "That's Angelica's balcony. All we have to do is jump."

Graham peered over the window ledge and paled. It was a good four-metre drop, and if I hadn't thought it was our only hope of solving several murders, I'd never have suggested it. But as far as I could see, we had no choice.

Graham may not be a big fan of extreme sports, but in an emergency he can be surprisingly brave. He didn't say a thing. Instead he swallowed hard, nodded, then swung a leg over the sill. He rolled onto his stomach and wrenched his other unwilling limb across before lowering himself down. He clung on by his fingertips for a moment, then let go. There was a loud splat as his bare feet hit the tiled floor of the balcony below.

"You OK?" I called softly. He looked at me and gave a half-hearted thumbs-up. He was bent almost double as if the fall had winded him, and was rubbing his left elbow, but he moved over to make way for me.

My turn. I did the same as Graham, landing awkwardly and feeling a bolt of pain shoot from ankle to knee. "Ouch!" I complained. "That hurt!"

"It was your idea," whispered Graham. "Let's hope it proves worthwhile."

There were heavy net curtains hanging across the French windows so we couldn't see into the room, but the door was open a fraction and it would be easy enough to get in. I took a deep breath to steel myself. I was pretty sure Angelica was innocent, but suppose I'd got it wrong? Josie had been stabbed to death with her own sandals. The viciousness of that attack made me feel suddenly nervous.

"Well," I said a little squeakily, "here goes."

I slid the door back, pulled aside the net curtain and Graham and I stepped through. It was dark inside compared with the sunlit balcony, and it took a few moments for our eyes to adjust.

We didn't have to go far in search of Angelica. She was sitting on the bed, staring at nothing, and as we approached she looked through us as if we were ghosts.

"Angelica?" I said uncertainly. "Can we talk to you?"

She made an effort to focus on me, wrenching her mind away from wherever it had been. She rubbed her eyes, shook her head and asked, "Me? You can't. No one's allowed to talk to me. Only Bill." Her eyes slid away again. This was going to be even harder than I'd thought. I was just wondering how to bring her back to the real world when Graham decided to speak up.

"Mrs Strummer?" he said. "We believe you're being framed. We'd very much like to know more about the personal assistant Bill employed before Tessa Whittam. I understand he was called Mick. Can you tell us anything about him?"

Angelica heaved the deepest sigh I've ever heard. It seemed to come up from the depths of the ocean. And then she said in a strange sing-song voice, "He wanted to see the bluebells."

The woman's mad, I thought. Unhinged. Deranged. Barking. There was no way we would get any sense out of her.

Then I recalled the photograph of her running through the woods, mouth open in a silent scream. Running through a bluebell wood, where the newly emerged flowers heads were just beginning to open.

And all of a sudden I caught the clue I'd been missing. It was like being doused with ice-cold water. I'd been so disconcerted by the embarrassing glimpse of her bra that I'd failed to see what was really wrong with that photo. Those bluebells were the key to everything.

I mean, you can't have a landscape gardener for a mother and not know that bluebells flower in the spring. And it had come unusually early this year. They'd started blooming the first week of April and had gone by the end of the month. Bill hadn't met Josie until June, which had to be at least six weeks after that photo was taken.

So why had Angelica been running through the woods screaming?

My mind went into overdrive, frantically recalculating. This changed everything. Before I had a chance to say anything, Graham pressed on.

"Mrs Strummer, we believe Tessa Whittam may be in love with your ex-husband."

"I'm sure she is," Angelica said in the same dreamy voice. She rocked backwards and forwards. "The whole world adores him. Everybody loves Bill. Everybody but me…"

My mouth dropped open but no sound came out. Everything had suddenly snapped into place. Graham didn't notice.

"We're wasting our time here," he said to me, looking over to the balcony. "Have you thought about how we can get back up to your room?"

Angelica rose from the bed and drifted like a sleepwalker out through the French windows and onto the balcony.

"Graham!" I beckoned him over to the door so we could talk without disturbing her. "All this time we've thought she's mad. But what if she isn't? Suppose she's been telling the truth?"

"What do you mean?" he asked.

"She keeps saying Bill loves her. I think she's right!"

Graham shook his head incredulously. "That can't be true. Bill married Josie. He wrote her that song."

"Did he? Are we sure of that? Think of all those other song titles, Graham – the ones from years back. Were *they* written for Angelica? "My One, My Only", "All Time and For Ever", "You Won't Never Need No One But Me", "I'm Yours, You're Mine, End of Story". Add them together – don't they sound a bit menacing? A bit obsessive? And the Christmas hit – "He Ain't the One for You" – what was that all about? And then "Ain't No Escaping My Love"? He's starting to sound like a stalker!"

Graham looked completely unconvinced, but by now I was bowling along like a runaway train.

"You know, when I read those newspapers I thought there was something a bit funny about those phrases Angelica's friends trotted out. They sounded like cheesy song lyrics – which is just how Bill speaks. All these people who were supposed to be so angry that they wouldn't come to Bill's wedding – why aren't they looking after Angelica? That's what friends are for, isn't it? How come they can talk to the newspapers but they can't talk to her? I reckon they don't exist. I bet Bill planted those stories to make people think Angelica was going mad. And it worked, too. *Everyone* thinks she's crazy. Including you," I finished accusingly.

We glanced over at Angelica. She was leaning on the parapet, twirling a strand of hair between her fingers, swaying and humming tunelessly to herself. Even I had to admit she looked pretty loopy.

"It's the bluebells, Graham. They flower in the spring. She was heartbroken, sure, but that picture has to have been taken at least a month before Bill met Josie. So whatever upset her then, it wasn't Bill leaving her."

Graham frowned. "If you're correct about the flowers – and I'm sure that with your horticultural expertise you are – it's very significant. And yet I don't understand. You say Bill loves Angelica. And Angelica clearly loves Bill. So why did he marry Josie?"

"*Does* Angelica love him, though? She just said everybody loves him but her."

"She's insane!" exclaimed Graham. "You heard what she said to Ruby. She was clearly still devoted to him."

I remembered Angelica's outburst the night we arrived. That cracked, dry sob. "I want him back. But I can't. Never, never, never…" There was no doubting the depth of her feelings. And yet…"

"OK. But suppose she wasn't talking about Bill? That song title – "He Ain't the One for You". What if she'd fallen in love with another man!"

"But who?"

"Who else died, Graham?" I demanded, slapping my hand against the wall. "We were right – the motive for the murders *is* jealousy. We just got the wrong culprit."

All the photographs of Bill and Angelica I'd seen in the newspapers flashed through my head like a slideshow. Bill standing next to Angelica, staring sullenly into the camera. I'd thought it was because he'd lost interest in his wife, but maybe he was seething with emotion. Just behind him had stood a man. I'd assumed it was a bodyguard, but it could easily have been Bill's PA, Mick. Angelica, her face full of love. Suppose Angelica wasn't looking adoringly up at Bill, but smiling over his shoulder at the person behind him? Bill's right-hand man – who might have felt more for Angelica than he was supposed to...

"Mick," I said. "She was in love with *Mick*. And then he died. That would explain why she was so upset in the bluebell wood."

"But why come here? Why try to stop the wedding?"

"I don't know. To save Josie from Bill?"

"Save *her*? You're not suggesting *he* was her murderer?"

I stared at Graham for a moment. It was the only solution that made sense. "Yes, I think he is," I said slowly, puzzling it out as I spoke. "All that Mr Nice Guy stuff? Bill seems so easy-going and laid-back – but you don't make it to the top of the showbiz ladder without being pushy, do you? He's just better at hiding it than most people. All this time we've been thinking Angelica was obsessed with Bill ... when it's the other way round! And if Angelica was planning to leave him – well, he could have killed Mick, couldn't he?"

Graham almost exploded in protest. "But he married Josie!"

"Yes! To get his revenge. This whole thing has been a set-up. All that Venus and Adonis stuff. Tessa said those costumes were Josie's idea. So did Bill. But Josie said her dress was Bill's choice. And that gold bikini – she looked like a kid in fancy dress. I bet he chose that, too. What if he planned the whole thing from beginning to end? The deal with *Hi!* magazine, all that press coverage… Those comments from outraged celebrities – he planted them! What if he wanted maximum media attention to draw Angelica out? To have her totally in his power. She's got no friends – he's seen to that over the years. "You Won't Never Need No One But Me." It doesn't get clearer than that, does it? *He's* the complete control freak, Graham! The only two people here who ever listened to Angelica are dead – he's seen to that too. He must have killed his own mother! And Sizal

– Bill must have thought he knew something about her and Mick. He's framed Angelica, good and proper. That's why she said that stuff about him visiting her in prison – *that's* why she sounded so defeated – she knows there's no way out. She tried to help but no one believed her. "Ain't No Escaping My Love" wasn't written for Josie: it was written to torment Angelica. Can you imagine her sitting up here, listening to it over and over again, knowing it was meant for her, knowing that he was going to do something to Josie and that nobody would believe her? No wonder the poor woman's gone bonkers!"

My voice had become louder and louder as I'd been talking. Angelica hadn't paid the blindest bit of attention, but clearly Gregor had. He must have alerted his employer to the fact that Angelica had visitors, because without warning the door swung open and Bill Strummer walked in. Graham and I were so shocked, we both screamed. It was enough to startle Angelica out of her reverie and she looked at Bill in terror. Then, before any of us could stop her, she scrambled onto the parapet.

There she stood, teetering on the edge for a second. And, with a last, despairing sob, she jumped.

no more mr nice guy

Bill roared like a tiger whose prey has escaped, then let out a stream of swear-words that could have made your ears bleed.

Graham and I raced across the room, leant over the parapet and saw, to our immense relief, that Angelica had landed in deep water. She bobbed to the surface but seemed to be making no effort to swim.

"You stupid—!" bellowed Bill from inside the room, and Graham and I spun round to face him. I'm not repeating what he called us – you can probably imagine.

It was obvious that *he* knew that *we* knew all about him. He must have been listening at the door while we worked it out. And now something was contorting his features: something that terrified the pants off me. It was the cold, savage rage that had clearly inspired him to stab Josie.

For the first time I noticed how extremely well-muscled his arms and shoulders were. We were two against one, but I doubted we'd stand much chance, especially as he'd just pulled a knife from his pocket and flicked it open.

"Come over here," he said, "and get what you deserve."

I looked at Graham. He gave me a faint nod and his eyes slid seawards. In that split second we made our decision.

Let me assure you, climbing over a parapet and plummeting – what, thirty metres? – into the sea is not a pleasant experience. Don't try it at home. The water whacked me so hard, it knocked the breath clean out of my lungs and I sank deep, deep down in a rush of bubbles, and soon I didn't know which way was up. I thrashed and kicked but couldn't tell if I was swimming deeper or back to the surface, and it was all just lung-bursting panic until a hand grabbed mine and pulled. That gulp of air as I broke through into the sunlight was the sweetest breath I've ever inhaled.

I looked around. Graham was treading water a

couple of metres away. The hand that had grabbed me belonged to Angelica.

The pair of us splashing down so close to her seemed to have jerked her out of her dream-like state. Letting her husband frame her was one thing. Allowing the deaths of two innocent children was quite another. Her face had taken on a determined look.

"Can you swim to the beach?" she demanded.

"Yes," I spluttered. It wasn't that far – just around the rocks – and it wasn't like there was a heavy current to contend with. Angelica struck out in a smooth crawl, and Graham and I kind of doggy-paddled behind, still winded by the long drop.

When we reached the cove we were faced with a new problem. Bill was already at the top of the path, descending fast, the knife glinting in his hand. He didn't look like he was after a cosy chat.

Our only hope was the pedalo. Graham and I began to pull it across the sand and Angelica pushed from the other side, but we were all so panicked by the sight of Bill that our teamwork wasn't exactly impressive. We reached the water's edge just as he reached the beach. He was less than ten metres away now, but the soft sand was harder for him to run on than the cliff path had been.

"Stop!" he screamed.

I took strength from the edge of fear in his voice: he must think he couldn't reach us in time. We gave the pedalo one last shove, then Graham and I jumped into the seats and started pedalling frantically while Angelica leapt onto the back.

Behind us Bill's heavy footsteps thudded over the last bit of dry sand and came splashing into the waves. Angelica stuck her legs in the water and kicked desperately to give us more momentum. Bill lunged, but her sudden spurt of energy took us beyond his reach. And thankfully Bill wasn't a good swimmer like Angelica. Once he found he was out of his depth, he turned back for land, defeated.

"If we can get round to the big beach there'll be loads of people," I puffed. "He can't do anything to us there."

For a while we pedalled along the shoreline in silence. But after five minutes or so I couldn't help asking, "It was Bill, wasn't it? He killed all of them. Starting with Mick."

The pedalo lurched as Angelica moved up to perch between me and Graham. "You know about him?" she said incredulously. "How?"

"Well … we kind of worked it out," I said. "It took a while, though. Bill's Mr Nice Guy act is very convincing."

"Tell me about it," she said wearily. "It was years before I saw through him. If I had done so sooner, Mick might still be alive."

"You shouldn't blame yourself," Graham put in helpfully. "Con men don't go around with flashing neon signs on their heads saying DON'T TRUST ME, I'M A GIT. They're charming. Likeable. Plausible. That's how people get taken in."

"Perhaps you're right. I was so young when we met! Just a kid, really. I didn't know any better." She let out a sad, tired laugh. "He made me ditch my friends. I thought it was romantic that he wanted me all to himself. Stupid girl! It was only later that I realized he had me in a stranglehold. Then along came Mick…"

"And you fell in love with him?"

"Head over heels. But Bill refused to give me a divorce – he said he'd never let me go. Mick tried to make him see sense, be reasonable, but he wouldn't. Then one day I couldn't take any more. I told him I was leaving and went to pack my case. Mick must have been out walking his dog. By the time I was ready to go, the police were at the door. As soon as I heard, I knew exactly what Bill had done. I couldn't think straight. I ran through the wood, I just had to find Mick. When I got back I was too distraught to tell the police what I thought had happened. After they left, Bill kept me prisoner. Locked me in my own home! And then he met Josie, and he worked out his little plan. After that he made sure no one believed a word I said. The more I protested, the crazier I looked. But I had to try. I knew the whole wedding was set up to trap me, but I had no choice. I had to come. That poor girl! She had no relatives, no friends to protect her. That's why Bill chose her."

"Did you tell Ruby all this?" I asked.

"Yes. She didn't believe me. And when I found her – when I saw what he'd done to his own mother – I knew Sizal would be at risk too. I used to talk to him sometimes, you see? I'd asked him to help me. But even *he* thought I'd gone mad. I ran back to the villa but I was too late. This morning I went down to plead with Josie again – I knew she wasn't safe – but she was already dead. I don't suppose she'd have believed me anyway: no one ever does. Even his mother couldn't see what Bill was really like…"

"But we can!" Graham said staunchly.

"Believing is one thing. Proving is another," said Angelica miserably. "If it was that easy, don't you think I'd have done something?"

"There's a photo of you taken that day in the bluebell wood…" I said. "You look dreadful."

Angelica let out a wry laugh. "Thanks."

"Sorry, but you know what I mean. It was taken before Bill met Josie. It proves you must have been upset about Mick, not about Bill leaving you for another woman. OK, it's not much, but it's a start. And we'll back you up."

We'd been pedalling for a good twenty minutes. My legs were starting to feel distinctly wobbly around the knees and Graham's breathing was ragged with effort. "Not far now," I puffed encouragingly. "If we can just get around the headland we'll be home and dry."

We neared the rocks, and, turning the corner, caught a glimpse of the golden stretch of sandy beach. My heart lifted for a moment. Then it sank to the bottom of the ocean. I could hear a speedboat engine. And I could see Bill powering towards us.

Angelica curled into a tight ball. "There's no escaping him," she whimpered. "He'll never let me go. Never! I won't be free of him until I'm dead!"

We didn't have time to argue with her before Bill's boat was on us, nudging the pedalo backwards, around the headland and out of sight of the beach. Then he powered up his engine and ploughed on, pushing our helpless little craft further and further out to sea. The pedals were now whirring round so hard and fast, we had to lift our legs high in the air for fear of having our feet chopped off. All we could do was cling on and wait for Bill to stop. And, in his own good time, he did.

Coolly, casually, as if he was picking up a mop or broom, Bill took a boat hook from the floor of his speedboat. He raised it above his head and then, with a force that might have been impressive if it hadn't been so terrifying, brought the pointed end down into pedalo, just centimetres from where Angelica was cowering. And in about five seconds flat, our heroic vessel started to sink.

I looked back at the island. We were at least a kilometre out to sea. There was no way I could swim that far, and neither could Graham. We were done for.

"You know, kids," Bill said, smiling his charming smile, "pedalos are dead dangerous. Ain't no escaping the currents around here."

"You won't get away with it!" Graham shouted as the pedalo finally gave up and began to disappear beneath the surface. We were ankle-deep. Knee-deep. Thigh-deep in water.

"Sure I will. Two drownings? Two more deaths by misadventure? Tragic, but not suspicious, I think you'll find."

We were treading water now. We couldn't even strike out for the shore with Bill's boat in the way.

He leant over the side and extended a hand to his ex-wife. "Come to me, angel," he said in a silky-smooth voice that made my flesh creep. "You know you want to."

Angelica let out a soft moan, but instead of swimming towards Bill she struck out determinedly in the opposite direction. Her long hair streamed behind her and Bill had only to reach down and grab it to haul her back. He held her there for a moment, a grin playing on his handsome features. He had her just where he wanted her. Then he bent down and plucked her from the sea as if she weighed nothing.

Angelica collapsed on the floor of the boat. All the fight seemed to have gone out of her. Bill booted up the engine, turned the vessel round and steered towards the shore. In no time at all they were ten, twenty, fifty metres away. Half-heartedly Graham and I started to swim, but we knew our chances of survival were zero.

Then, suddenly, Angelica struck. I don't know what she'd found to use as a weapon, but it must have been good and hard. We couldn't see exactly what happened – just a figure leaping at the pilot. He staggered, and the engine sputtered and died. She struck again. There was a yell of pain, a splash, a desperate, angry roar. Bill was in the water, trying to haul himself back on board. But the engine started again and the boat lurched sideways, out of control, out of his reach. Angelica had clearly never steered a speedboat before: it was all over the place, spinning in a circle, shooting off, turning ... then heading in a straight line for the man in the water.

Bill let out a high, hideous scream, which was cut short when the boat thudded into him. He didn't make another sound, and when the boat had passed over where he'd been, he didn't bob back to the surface. Instead we saw red spreading across the water. It looked like someone had poured a can of paint into the sea.

Graham and I grimaced in horror but didn't say a word: we were saving our breath for swimming.

We didn't need to. Angelica had finally got the boat under control. Five minutes later she had plucked us from the water and we were heading for the shore.

There's not much to add, really. Tessa clearly *had* had ambitions to become the third Mrs Strummer. When Graham and I returned to the villa with Angelica, dripping wet and with a long story for the police, she was None Too Pleased. We gave our statements, a bemused Sally standing by as the Responsible Adult, her eyes growing wider by the second. "I am never, ever taking you two anywhere again," she told us afterwards – which I didn't think was very fair. It wasn't us who'd committed all those murders. "What on earth will your mother say? No – don't tell me. I can imagine. You'll be lucky if she ever lets you out of her sight in future."

After paying Sally an enormous wad of cash in tight-lipped silence, Tessa despatched us off the island as fast as she could. Somehow I suspected she wouldn't get in touch with her old college friend a second time.

When the news got out about Josie's murder she was elevated to heights of fame that she could only have dreamt about while she was still alive. She became the embodiment of tragically doomed youth and beauty – standing somewhere between Marilyn Monroe and Princess Diana. It can't have been much compensation for being murdered by the man she'd had a crush on since she was seven.

Overnight, Bill went from being rock-star-superhero-who-does-so-much-for-charity to murdering-scum-of-the-earth-who-deserved-everything-he-got. While his reputation nosedived, Angelica's rocketed into the stratosphere.

She seemed to develop a new lease of life. With our evidence backing her version of events, her story was accepted not only by the police but by the public at large. Everyone wanted to know her side of things and she suddenly found herself invited to chat shows all over the world.

Mick's dog, Dinkum, was freed from the canine equivalent of death row, where he'd been languishing since Mick's so-called accident, and was rehomed with

Angelica. It was good to know that one innocent life had been spared.

The fact that Angelica had steered a speedboat over her ex-husband didn't seem to bother anyone unduly. She claimed it was an accident and everybody believed her. Well, almost everybody. Graham and I weren't convinced. I mean, she'd managed to handle the boat well enough when she rescued us. We didn't say anything, though. We couldn't exactly blame her after everything she'd been through. And if *she* hadn't killed *him*, *we'd* both have drowned. Bill suffering death by misadventure seemed like poetic justice.

The rock star had left his entire fortune to Angelica but she didn't want to touch a penny of it – she gave everything away to good causes. A large chunk went to the children's home where Josie had been brought up and they erected a really nice memorial to her in the garden.

Meanwhile, Angelica made her own fortune by writing her autobiography. *Please Believe Me* became an international bestseller. It was dedicated to Mick. And to me and Graham.

Has the past come back to haunt them?

mondays
are
murder

zombies?
spooks?
or just plain murder?

tanya landman

My name is Poppy Fields. I never
believed in ghosts – until I stayed on
a remote Scottish island, and people
started dropping dead all over the
place. Was a spirit taking revenge? When
Graham and I investigated, we began to
see right through it...

That's the way to do it!

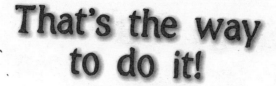

dead
funny

can you
die laughing?

tanya landman

My name is Poppy Fields. I was dead excited
about my first trip to America. But then
people started getting themselves killed in
really weird ways. Nothing made sense
until Graham and I investigated, then the
murders seemed to tie together as neatly
as a string of sausages. A little *too* neatly...

3

Stage fright!

who'll be left in
the final act?

dying
to be
famous

tanya landman

My name is Poppy Fields. When Graham
and I landed parts in a musical, we didn't
expect real drama. But then the star got a
death threat and the bodies started
stacking up. Before we knew it, we were
at the top of the murderer's list...

the
head is
dead

school won't kill you –
will it?

tanya landman

My name is Poppy Fields. When we
designed a murder mystery trail
for the school fayre, it was supposed
to be a bit of fun. But before long
the head was dead and Graham and
I were hunting down a real life killer.

Murder is a beastly business!

the
scent
of
blood

someone's about to become
dead meat...

tanya landman

My name is Poppy Fields. Graham and
I were first on the scene at a series
of murders at the zoo, but who
was behind them? We had to prowl
around a bit to investigate – and what
we saw was not pretty. How would
we escape before we, too, became
dead meat?

My name is Poppy Fields. When the circus came to town, the posters promised certain death. This made Grahma and me suspicious, and we were proved right when someone was killed in the ring. With the circus performers still in grave danger, we had to work fast to discover who was firing the shots...

Words can be dangerous.

WITHDRAWN

beginning,
middle...
sticky end!

poison
pen

'Red House Children's Book Award Winner'

tanya landman

My name is Poppy Fields. When we
offered to help out at our local literary
festival, Graham and I had no idea just
how murky the world of children's
books really was. Before you could say
crime novel, the authors were receiving
anonymous threats. Then fiction
started turning into fact...

Simone Cave was the health editor at the *Daily Mirror* for eight years and is now a freelance journalist covering health and medical issues for national newspapers and magazines. She lives with her husband and three children in South London. Simone can be contacted via: www.yourbabyandchild.com

Dr Caroline Fertleman is a Consultant Paediatrician at the Whittington Hospital and also works at the Institute of Child Health (UCL) and has an honorary contract with Great Ormond Street Hospital. She lives in London with her husband and three children.

Potty
Training
Girls

... the easy way

Simone Cave and
Dr Caroline Fertleman

Vermilion
LONDON

5 7 9 10 8 6

Published in 2009 by Vermilion, an imprint of Ebury Publishing

Ebury Publishing is a Random House Group company

Copyright © Simone Cave and Dr Caroline Fertleman 2009

Simone Cave and Dr Caroline Fertleman have asserted their right to be
identified as the authors of this Work in accordance with the Copyright,
Designs and Patents Act 1988.

The Random House Group Limited Reg. No. 954009

Addresses for companies within the Random House Group can be found at
www.randomhouse.co.uk

A CIP catalogue record for this book is available from the British Library

The Random House Group Limited supports The Forest Stewardship
Council (FSC®), the leading international forest certification organisation.
Our books carrying the FSC label are printed on FSC® certified paper.
FSC is the only forest certification scheme endorsed by the leading
environmental organisations, including Greenpeace.
Our paper procurement policy can be found at:
www.randomhouse.co.uk/environment

MIX
Paper from
responsible sources
FSC
www.fsc.org
FSC® C016897

Printed and bound by CPI Group (UK) Ltd, Croydon, CR0 4YY

ISBN 9780091929145

Copies are available at special rates for bulk orders. Contact the sales
development team on 020 7840 8487 for more information.

To buy books by your favourite authors and register for offers, visit
www.randomhouse.co.uk

We dedicate this book to our daughters
Natalie and Betsy.

CONTENTS

ACKNOWLEDGEMENTS

With thanks to:

Paul Johnson, Judy Cave and Barbara Levy.

Introduction

Little girls are known to be sensible, mature and generally more advanced than little boys the same age. This is because their brains actually develop earlier than boys'. Boys tend to use just the left-hand side of their brain, which thinks analytically. Girls use both the left-hand side and also the creative right-hand side at the same time because the neural pathway between the left and right side is more efficient. This is why girls generally develop language skills earlier, and this difference continues until the age of five when boys catch up. If this sounds like your daughter, it certainly bodes well for potty training. With a bit of encouragement from you she should leave her nappies behind with a minimum of fuss and puddles.

Unfortunately, things don't always go by the book. Life can get in the way of the most carefully laid plans. It's well known, for instance, that stressful events such as a new sibling or moving house can have a big impact on potty training. Also, although you hear fewer problems about girls learning to use the potty, all children are different; just because your child is female it doesn't guarantee she will be mature and sensible. Plenty of little girls are boisterous, slower to mature and struggle to concentrate.

We've taken all this into account and have written this book to guide you gently through the process of potty training, whatever your situation. Our flexible approach makes the transition from nappies to the toilet smooth, stress-free and fun for all little girls. If you hit a stumbling block, we'll show you step by step how to deal with the problem. By following our potty-training programme your daughter will learn to use the potty in just a couple of weeks – or, if you're particularly lucky, even sooner.

It tends to be Mum who potty trains her daughter, but anyone caring for your little girl can use this book. We've included a special section for dads – it's not always easy for fathers to take their young daughters to the toilet so we've given lots of tips.

WHAT AGE SHOULD SHE BEGIN?

This is the million-dollar question. In the UK, the average age for little girls is around two and a quarter (two and a half for boys). As all children are different your daughter may not be ready to potty train until she is older – sometimes nearer her third birthday than her second. She may, however, be ready from as young as 18 months. There's nothing you can do to change the age at which she develops and becomes ready – this is down to nature. What you *can* do is observe her carefully and spot the signs that she's ready to begin (*see Chapter 1*).

Getting the timing right is key to successful potty training. If you push your daughter too early she'll probably take longer to learn, and may even have to go back into nappies for a few weeks. A US study published in the journal *Pediatrics* found that training before the age of 27 months nearly always takes longer than training a child after this age.

Don't be in too much of a rush – it's not a competition. Your daughter won't turn around in 20 years and thank you for the fact that she was out of nappies three months earlier than her best friend. On the other hand, she may well have something to say about the fact that you pushed her into using the potty too soon and she ended up getting stressed and frustrated, still wetting herself at the age of five.

Be patient, wait until your daughter is ready, and the process will be swift with no tears.

OUR METHOD

Our method consists of having potty-training 'sessions', beginning with just an hour a day without a nappy and gradually building up until your daughter never wears a nappy at home during the day. The next stage is to leave the house without a nappy (*see Chapter* 6).

It's a very gentle approach that can be fitted around a busy schedule, even if you work full time or have other children. You don't have to do a 'session' every day – our method will work if you just manage weekends and perhaps a couple of sessions during the week at bath time. Unlike more intensive methods which take an all-or-nothing approach, there's no need to take a week off work and cancel social engagements while you spend time locked indoors with your daughter mopping up accidents. Our much more laid-back approach allows potty training to fit around your family and situation.

FRONT BOTTOM, URETHRA OR WEE-WEE HOLE?

Choosing a 'name' for girls' bits is never easy. You'll need to think of something by the time your daughter is about one because this is the age she'll probably start playing with herself on the changing table. There's no need to stop her doing this because it's entirely normal – it's natural, inquisitive behaviour. She is just exploring in the same way that she may also have discovered and played with her toes, hair or belly button. It's a good opportunity to begin teaching her the name of her different body parts.

While urethra is the anatomically correct name for the opening from which urine comes, most little girls won't like this term. Another downside of getting too technical is that you could find yourself having to refer to the vagina, labia and perineum. This would result in a lot of complicated names for a young child to learn, and even if she manages, chances are few other people will understand what she's talking about – particularly her peers.

Try to think of something easy to understand that your daughter will be comfortable saying at school. It's also got to be appropriate to say in front of your GP, as well as other family members. We've found that 'wee hole' is a good choice – it's an accurate description and yet sounds suitably childish. You can then also refer to 'poo hole' and, when it arises, 'baby hole'.

Other choices that work include front and back passage – again simple but accurate descriptions. The good old-fashioned 'front bottom' is still remarkably popular, as is 'fanny', although this is considered a bit rude by some. If you're travelling to the US, it's worth remembering that Americans use 'fanny' as a slang word for the bottom. There are all sorts of other nicknames, including 'twinkle' and 'minkie', which are fine to use if this is what your family is comfortable with. However, do give your daughter an alternative name for when she starts nursery and school so that she won't risk being teased.

You may also decide to call urine and faeces 'wee' and 'poo' – as we have done in this book. Everyone understands these terms including teachers, doctors and children.

1

Is She Ready?

1

Is She Ready?

If you try to coax your daughter out of nappies before she's ready you may run into problems. As we've said before, the average age for little girls to come out of nappies is about two and a quarter, but how do you know if your daughter is going to be one of the early ones or if she needs to wait a bit longer? Well, there are lots of signs to watch out for which indicate she is both physically and mentally ready (*see below*). If you monitor your daughter closely and get the timing right, you'll find that potty training only takes a couple of weeks with very few accidents.

Although it's known that girls are easier to train than boys, the downside of this is that it puts more pressure on them to come out of nappies earlier. So it's particularly important with girls to ignore competitive friends and family who tell you when they think your daughter should start using the potty. The very best person to decide when the time is right is you.

Even your daughter may be keen to come out of nappies before she's physically ready. However enthusiastic she is about using a potty, if she's not physically developed enough to be able to know when she needs a wee or poo then she's going to have accidents. This can be particularly upsetting for little girls because most are keen to get things right and to please their parents. You'll have to persuade her to wait a couple of months without dampening her enthusiasm. Explain to her that her bladder ('the bag in her tummy where her wee is stored') isn't yet strong enough but it will be very soon, and when it is she can have a go at using the potty. If your daughter is reluctant to take no for an answer then you could also try pull-up nappies. You can call them 'big girl knicker nappies' and let your daughter help pull them on.

CHECKLIST

Signs that She's Physically Ready

☐ **She is able to walk and is stable on her feet.** This is because learning to walk requires intense concentration as your daughter discovers how to use her voluntary muscles. It's too much to expect her to be consistently aware of her bodily functions as well (needing to wee and poo). It would simply overload her system if she had to learn to use the potty at the same time as learning to walk.

☐ **Her bowel muscles are fully developed.** From as young as eight months you'll notice that your little girl starts pooing at around the same time each day and poos less frequently than when she was a tiny baby. This is because her bowel muscles are developing. By the time she is two, she'll probably be going once or twice a day. But still go ahead with potty training even if your daughter doesn't quite fit this pattern because everybody's different when it comes to bowel movements.

☐ **Her bladder muscles are fully developed.** Bladder muscles mature later than the bowel, usually between 20 months and two years. You'll notice that your daughter has fewer wet nappies until eventually she can go for about three hours or longer without weeing. This is because the urethral sphincter muscles become more developed – these are the muscles that hold urine in the bladder, and as they strengthen your daughter will develop bladder control.

☐ **She's aware that she's doing a wee or a poo.** Between the ages of 18 months and two years, your little girl will develop awareness that she's going to the toilet. This generally happens a few months earlier with girls than with boys. Your daughter may start telling you that she's doing a wee or a poo, or perhaps she'll stop playing and squat. She may also tell you when her nappy is wet or soiled.

Signs that She's Mentally Ready

☐ **She's happy to have a go at sitting on a potty.** Children need to be mature enough to actually want to use the potty or toilet before you can start training them.

☐ **She's interested in other people going to the toilet.** Girls tend to show interest several months earlier than boys, which is one of the reasons they tend to come out of nappies sooner.

☐ **She can talk.** As well as being mentally mature enough to begin potty training, your daughter also needs adequate language development so that you can talk to each other about if and when she needs the toilet; and she'll need to understand your instructions and all the praise when she succeeds. As we've already mentioned, language is another area where girls are ahead of boys.

GETTING THE TIMING RIGHT

Timing is important when it comes to potty training. In an ideal world we would all pick a time when we're just following our normal routines because this is when stress levels tend to be lowest. If you've got a big event looming, such as a new baby or moving house, then ideally you should postpone potty training until afterwards.

With girls you can sometimes make exceptions. This is because girls tend to find potty training less stressful than boys. Indeed, some little girls learn to use the potty so quickly that it's easy enough to get them trained before big life events. It can be very convenient to get your little girl out of nappies before, say, a new baby arrives.

Wait a Few Months if...

- Your daughter has ever shown reluctance about sitting on a potty or been worried about the toilet flushing. This shows that she is likely to find potty training quite stressful. Coupled with the stress of a big event, it could all get a bit much for her.
- Your daughter is anxious about an up-and-coming event – for example, she knows you're moving house and seems to be having more tantrums.
- You feel you've got enough to cope with for the moment and having to deal with potty training as well would be just too much stress.

Go for It if…

- She can walk, talk (or at least say enough single words to make herself understood), is aware of doing a wee or poo and is enthusiastic about potties. If she's showing all the physical and mental signs listed above and is eager to give it a try then she'll probably learn very quickly.

- She's not having many tantrums or playing up. This indicates that she's happy and not anxious about anything.

- She's able to concentrate and doesn't lose patience with what she's doing. For example, she will calmly spend time doing puzzles even if she finds them difficult. This shows that she enjoys learning so is unlikely to find potty training too frustrating when she has accidents.

If you decide to 'go for it', do be prepared to abandon potty training after a couple of days if it turns out that your daughter isn't ready. This is particularly important if you're attempting to squeeze it in before a big event as stress levels will be higher. So if your daughter doesn't seem to be picking it up quickly, gets confused about when she's about to wee or poo and doesn't ask for the potty, then you'll have to face the fact that she probably isn't ready.

Don't make too much of stopping potty training. Simply say something like, 'That was fun, wasn't it? Perhaps we'll have another go after the baby is born.' Even if she's not yet ready, there's still plenty you can teach her so that when she does finally come out of nappies the process is as seamless as possible. In the next chapter, we explain how to help your daughter prepare to begin potty training.

Training in Time for Nursery

If your daughter is going to start pre-school nursery at the age of three, she'll be expected to be potty trained. Although most little girls are trained long before their third birthday, if your daughter is slower to mature then you'll feel pressurised by this nursery 'deadline' to get her out of nappies.

Try not to pass this pressure on to your daughter because it will delay things further. Call the nursery and explain what stage she is at with toilet training and they will probably put your mind at rest. They are so used to accidents that they will even have a box of spare clothes.

If they don't sound very understanding, then we advise postponing your daughter's nursery place for a term or even choosing a different, more understanding nursery (it's often possible to get a place at the last minute because other parents may change their plans and pull out). A few months won't make any difference in the long term. It's important that she doesn't get upset by unsympathetic teachers if she has lots of accidents. Once the pressure is off, you'll feel a lot more relaxed. Your daughter will pick up on this and will probably learn to use the toilet very quickly.

Do bear in mind that boys tend to have more accidents at nursery than girls, so the teachers won't be expecting your daughter to need constant reminding about the toilet or to have frequent accidents. It's important to mention to them if she needs a bit of help.

It's also common for children to regress in the weeks leading up to the start of term because they feel a bit anxious about going to nursery. Don't worry too much if your daughter is suddenly having lots of accidents; there's every chance that once she starts nursery she'll quickly improve.

Our final tip is to take her to the toilet when you arrive at the nursery, especially if she's not yet accident-free. She'll enjoy the child-sized toilets and low sinks used in nurseries and will soon get used to them. If she's at nursery for only a few hours, the chances are she won't need the toilet again until you pick her up. Don't worry if she does wet herself at nursery (or even soil her pants). Most children have accidents, particularly during their first term, so the staff will be geared up for it.

2

Early Preparation
for Potty Training

From around the age of one, your daughter will start to watch and learn what happens when you go to the loo. So, even if your little girl isn't yet ready to begin potty training (*see Chapter 1*), there's plenty you can do to help her in the meantime. Follow our tips and by the time you take your daughter out of nappies she'll not only be familiar and comfortable with bodily functions, but will be able to understand how to use the toilet too.

TIPS FOR PREPARING FOR POTTY TRAINING

Take her to the Loo with You

You probably already take your little girl to the toilet sometimes because it's more convenient than leaving her outside. Don't stop as your daughter gets older because the more familiar she is with the toilet, the quicker she'll learn to use it herself when the time is right, and the less likely she is to be afraid. You'll find that sometimes she will be more interested in playing with the toilet paper than watching you, but at other times she'll be fascinated by what you're doing. Don't be embarrassed; she's just curious in the same innocent way that she's curious if you put on mascara or make a phone call. Chat away about what you're doing and make sure that you wipe from front to back because your daughter will eventually imitate you.

When you wash your hands, encourage your daughter to do the same. This will instil good habits and make the whole process of going to the toilet into a fun game. You can also let her climb on to the toilet at home (when the seat is down) and flush it. Make this a bit of a treat, saying, 'You're such a big girl, would you like to flush the toilet?' This will increase her confidence and reduce the chances of her ever becoming frightened of sitting on the loo, or being 'sucked away' down a flushing toilet.

Public Toilets

When you're out with your daughter and need the loo, the easiest way to take her into a public toilet with you is to choose a disabled toilet and wheel her buggy in. This isn't always an option, however, so you may need to hold her in one arm and go to the loo one-handed – not easy but just about possible if you're desperate.

Once your daughter can walk and is too heavy to hold, she'll be busy playing with the lock on the door and the sanitary bin while you go to the loo. Try not to get cross because it's important that your daughter doesn't associate toilets with being told off. Instead you could give your daughter a 'job' such as holding your handbag, and if she still insists on squeezing round the back of the toilet and touching the seat, make sure that you wash her hands thoroughly afterwards.

It's important that you wipe the seat of public toilets and sit down, rather than squat. Again, your daughter will be watching closely and will imitate you when she's old enough, and she won't be able to squat over a toilet because she'll be too short.

Show Your Daughter her Dirty Nappy

From time to time, show your little girl her dirty nappy and chat about how you're putting on a fresh nappy and cleaning the poo off her bottom. Let her feel the heavy weight of a wet nappy and explain that it is heavier than a dry nappy because she's done lots of wee. This will give your daughter the message that going to the toilet is a natural process and nothing to be ashamed of. It's important to convey this, so don't ever show feelings of revulsion if you're changing a particularly smelly or leaky nappy.

Don't Get Angry if Your Little Girl 'Plays with Poo'

If you've ever walked into your little girl's nursery and discovered that she's taken off her nappy and smeared poo over her cot, herself and the walls, your natural reaction will have been horror, shock and revulsion. Surely little girls just don't do this sort of thing? Well, unfortunately some do (and boys too) but it doesn't mean that she's got behavioural problems, and she's certainly not being naughty. She's just being curious. Plenty of children do this – some even taste their poo!

It's important that you remain calm while you clean up, however much you want to yell and scream, because your daughter will be confused if you're angry about her poo. Getting very cross can occasionally lead to 'withholding constipation' (*see Chapter 9*), a condition that can affect toddlers if their carers have shown revulsion about their nappies and poos.

If your daughter repeatedly removes her nappy, put her sleep suit on back-to-front so that she can't reach the poppers.

Ensure that Carers are Comfortable Changing Your Daughter's Nappy

Scientists have shown that mums object to the smell of their own baby's poo less than that of other people's babies. In a study published in the *Journal of Evolution and Human Behaviour* (July 2006), mums were given 'anonymous' nappies to smell, and they found the smell of their own baby's nappy 'less revolting' than those of other babies.

It's thought that the 'disgust instinct' is overridden in mums to encourage them to nurture their babies – they would be less likely to do so if they found them repellent. This research demonstrates that carers may genuinely find changing your daughter's nappy more disgusting than you do. So be aware of this and ensure that people caring for your baby don't have any hang-ups that your daughter could pick up on.

Use Bath Time for Practice

Keep a potty in the bathroom from the time your daughter is about 15 months old so that she can play with it before her bath when she's naked. Tell her what the potty is for and that she can sit on it if she wants to. Your daughter may also like to sit on the potty fully clothed and imitate you when you go to the loo, so keep the potty near your toilet.

She's almost certainly too young to actually use her potty, but it's good to have one around so that she's familiar with it. Don't worry if she's not interested. You've got months before you will potty train her and there's no need to get stressed in the meantime. Let her become curious in her own time and don't try and force it. If she does happen to sit on it, then do give her lots of praise.

Your daughter is bound to wee in the bath but you usually won't notice because she'll be sitting. Never try and stop her because it would give negative messages. From 12 months onwards she may stand up more in the bath, especially if you use a non-slip bath mat. If you happen to notice her weeing, point it out, saying, 'You're doing a wee, what a clever girl.' This will help your daughter to become aware of when she's weeing, and awareness is the first step to control.

Make Use of her Dolls

Dolls can be useful throughout the toilet-training programme. Girls have an advantage over boys in that most of them love dolls. You can buy dolls that wee and have potties, which can be helpful in encouraging your daughter to understand the potty-training process. Any doll can help her learn, however, because you can encourage her to sit it on the potty that you keep in the bathroom. It's a known teaching technique to allow the pupil to teach someone else the skill they are trying to acquire.

Helping your daughter to be aware of potties, toilets and bodily functions will give her a big advantage when she starts to actually use the potty. She will already have a pretty good idea about the 'theory' of potty training and all she'll have to do is put it into practice.

3

Countdown to
the Big Day

When your daughter is showing signs that she is both physically and mentally ready to begin potty training and you know that D-day is imminent (*see Chapter 1*), there are several steps to take. You must prepare your daughter for what's about to happen; prepare your home; and finally take your daughter on a shopping spree to buy the kit such as knickers and stickers. Here's our guide to gearing up for the big day.

PREPARE YOUR DAUGHTER

When you're both feeling relaxed, tell your daughter that you think she's ready to stop wearing nappies quite soon. If you have followed our tips in Chapter 2 she'll have a reasonable understanding of potties and what they are for, and there's a good chance that she will be keen to try using one.

Talk her through the process and *ask* her if she'd like to give potty training a go. Explain that you'll have to go to the shops together to choose potties and knickers. She'll probably be very enthusiastic, but if she's not ready and seems reluctant, that's fine. Tell her that she can wait a few more weeks if she wants to. Some little girls need a bit longer to get their heads around starting something new, and it's much better to let them be ready in their own time than to push.

Once she has agreed to give potty training a try then tell her when the shopping trip will be, and also talk her through what will happen when she has an accident. Explain that she may accidentally wee or poo on the floor or in her new knickers from time to time while she's learning. Emphasise that this is okay because you'll clean it up with wipes and so on, and put the soiled knickers in the washing machine then give her some nice clean ones to wear. It really helps little girls to understand the process of accidents and cleaning up before the event because they can become quite upset if they make a mess or 'spoil' their new knickers.

PREPARE YOUR HOME

Choose the room in which you want to begin potty training. If you have a room with old carpets or a floor that's easy to clean, this may be an obvious choice. Make sure the 'training room' is warm enough – you may need to turn up the heating by a couple of degrees during the winter months because your daughter will be semi-naked in the early stages of potty training.

You can use plastic-backed bathmats to protect your floor and sofa, with your daughter sitting on the soft side. If you don't want to risk your carpet getting soiled you can always set up a play area in the corner of the kitchen, if it's big enough. Using the garden is another good option if it's warm enough to play outside. Lots of mums wait until the summer to get their toddlers out of nappies – as well as sparing your carpets, there's less washing because children wear fewer clothes in the warmer months. However, there's no need to be limited to the summer because when your daughter is ready to begin, she'll learn to use the potty and toilet very quickly and there shouldn't be many accidents.

GO SHOPPING

Once your little girl has given you the go-ahead that she wants to start using the potty, you can go shopping together for knickers and toilet-training equipment. Talk to her about this shopping trip in advance so that she can look forward to it and have a few days to think about and get used to the idea of coming out of nappies. By the time you hit the shops she'll be very enthusiastic and will love choosing pretty knickers and fancy star charts.

Shopping List

Here are some useful potty-training gadgets worth buying. Let your daughter make some of the choices, although she obviously doesn't have to be present for every purchase.

Two Identical Cheap Plastic Potties

We strongly advise getting two identical potties because you can keep one in the play area and one in the bathroom and you'll avoid a situation where your daughter refuses point blank to use the 'red' potty. If you've already got a potty in the bathroom that's fine because there's no harm in having spare potties that you can keep around your home.

Cheap plastic potties are ideal because they're small and easy to clean. Also, your daughter will squat right down on the floor with her feet on the ground – this is a better position for pooing than sitting on a larger-style potty. Don't worry about potties having splashguards on them; these are to stop boys making too much mess but won't affect your daughter in any way. She can sit with the splashguard at the front or the back, whichever she chooses. Your little girl should definitely be involved in choosing her potty, but you'll have to steer her away from the larger, fancy potties. She'll still enjoy selecting the colour.

Knickers

Do let her have her say in what she wants. She may opt for something pretty and girly, or choose her favourite television character like Dora the Explorer. We've found that if she likes her knickers she'll not only be keener to wear them, but also to keep them dry. If she can't make up her mind then buy a couple of packs – they'll get plenty of use, especially if you buy knickers in a size bigger than her age (we recommend doing this as it makes it much easier to pull them up and down).

Big Leggings and Tights

Most children don't have the manual dexterity to cope with buttons and complicated clothes until they are about four. So stock up on leggings (not too tight) as these are easy to pull up and down, enabling your daughter to go to the toilet alone when the time comes. Tights in a larger size than she normally wears are also helpful – these will be easier for you to yank down quickly and also easier for your daughter to manage by herself as she progresses. Elasticised trousers also work, and jogging-style bottoms are a very practical, albeit unfeminine, option.

Pretty Stickers

Little girls love stickers so hunt out some that she hasn't had before and thinks are a bit special. A reward chart helps spur on most girls – you can buy a ready-made chart from large supermarkets and stationers. Alternatively, make your own using a thick piece of A4 paper or card. Write a list of training achievements down one side, such as sitting on the potty; doing a wee in the potty; doing a poo in the potty; pulling down knickers; pulling up knickers; washing hands. You can draw simple pictures for each of these activities then draw horizontal lines across the card so that each activity has its own space for stars and stickers. Every time your little girl completes an activity, she gets a star or sticker – you can buy these, or just draw on stars.

A Mini Toilet Seat

Children can find sitting on the loo quite frightening because it's high up and large enough for them to fall down. So it's important to get your daughter a child's toilet seat that scales down the toilet to her size. We particularly recommend those with side handles as these give your daughter something to hold on to.

A Stepping Stool

This will help your daughter climb on to the toilet, and then she can rest her feet on it for added security. She can also use it to reach the sink to wash her hands. You can buy cheap plastic stools designed for this purpose.

A Folding Toilet Seat

This can be helpful when you're out and about because your daughter will feel more secure sitting on a 'smaller' toilet. It will also be more hygienic for her, although you will have to wipe the public toilet seat first so that you don't get your portable seat too dirty. You can buy padded travel seats. Plastic ones are less comfortable but fold smaller.

A Travel Potty

These are particularly useful in the early stages of potty training when your daughter won't have the physical capacity to hold on for more than a minute or two before she wees. The folding potty frame can be whipped out, the legs unfolded, and then you put a bag over the top with a liner at the bottom – or you can put the bag and liner on before you leave home to save time. Once your daughter has been to the toilet you simply throw the bag away. You can also get portable potties with lids. We don't recommend these, however, as they are bulkier and you probably won't want to carry around your daughter's wee and poo.

Try to begin potty training within a few days of your shopping spree while your little girl is enthusiastic. Help her to put her new knickers away, and to put her new potties in place ready to begin. She can start using her stepping stool to wash her hands straight away. Do let her play with her 'new toys' if she wants to.

Don't Waste Your Money on the Following

Fancy Potties

Don't fork out on themed potties including musical ones or those shaped like animals. If your daughter needs this sort of persuasion to sit on the potty she's simply not ready to come out of nappies. Also, it's important that her potty isn't so appealing that she won't switch to the toilet – we encourage her to start using the toilet within the first couple of weeks of our training programme.

Imitation Toilet Potties

Avoid these cumbersome toilet lookalikes, which are large and have lids. They may be more comfortable and appealing to some children, but as we said above, our programme moves from the potty to the real toilet within a couple of weeks so it's not worth spending lots of money on these big potties. They can also be more difficult to clean than a small plastic potty.

Training Pants

These absorbent cloth pants look and feel like real knickers, but they will make your daughter feel wetter than if she was wearing a nappy. The idea is that your daughter will become more aware of when she is weeing and pooing. We think they're a waste of time because when your daughter is truly ready to begin toilet training she'll know when she's weeing and pooing in her nappy anyway. Training pants tend to be used before children are really ready to come out of nappies. It's harder to clean up soiled training pants than a soiled nappy, which you can simply throw away.

Pull-ups

Pull-up nappies are marketed as the most grown-up style of nappy for toddlers. We think that they're a bit of a gimmick and tend to be more expensive. That said, we sometimes recommend them for night-time (when your daughter still needs a nappy at night but feels too grown up to wear one), and also for the occasions when your daughter is insisting on being a big girl and wearing her knickers but you want her to wear a nappy, such as when you're travelling in a car, train or plane.

Don't Try and Take Shortcuts

You may have heard of children who skip the potty stage and instead go directly from nappies to using the toilet. Okay, this avoids having to clean poo-filled potties, and cuts out a step in the potty-training process, but we think it's better to use a potty. In our programme your little girl will move pretty swiftly from a potty to the toilet, but the advantage of getting her on a potty initially is that it puts her in a squatting position which helps pooing. Also, she will be more likely to sit for longer on a potty, which increases her chances of success. Another advantage is that you won't need to stand over and hold her to help her balance as you would with a toilet.

The only exception we make is if your daughter is big for her age, in which case the potty will be very uncomfortable (*see Chapter 5*).

We recommend keeping the potty-training process as simple as possible and just buying what you need to make it a bit more convenient. So although there's a lot of paraphernalia out there, there's no need to get carried away when you shop.

4

D-day

So the day has arrived when the nappy comes off and the puddles begin. This can be a bit daunting for both parents and children. This is why our training method has potty-training 'sessions' that last for only about an hour. So there's no need to cancel your social life or take time off work.

It's all very simple. During a session, your daughter goes without her nappy at home then at the end of the session you put it back on again. The method has been devised to cut the stress of potty training to an absolute minimum. This is important because your little girl shouldn't pick up on any stress and should never feel that by having accidents she is disappointing you. She will progress a lot more quickly if the process is kept very positive.

Some little girls will learn to use the potty in a few days using our method. By all means watch your daughter closely and, if she seems able, you can extend the length and number of potty-training sessions quite quickly. However, it's more likely to take a couple of weeks to get the hang of things.

We suggest that you hold back from taking your daughter out without her nappy on for a couple of weeks after she's got the hang of using the potty and toilet at home. It's obviously more challenging to find a public toilet for girls than boys (who can wee down drains or in the gutter). Girls can be particularly sensitive to having accidents and often feel more self-conscious than boys, so rather than put your daughter through any unnecessary stress we advise waiting a little longer before going out in public without a nappy.

Plenty of little girls have had success using a more intense potty-training method – the all-or-nothing approach where they stop wearing a nappy and that's it. There's no switching from pants to nappies, even when you leave the house. You just go for it and hope for the best. Some experts argue that it's confusing to keep swapping from pants to nappies, but we haven't found this. After all, children seem to cope with wearing a nappy at night and pants during the day.

Using our potty-training sessions approach, you will probably have your daughter out of nappies within a few weeks. Within a few months there's a good chance that you won't even bother to pack spare knickers when you go out.

BEFORE YOU BEGIN

Choose a Time

Pick a morning when you and your daughter are feeling happy and relaxed then suggest, 'Shall we have a go at using the potty today?' A good time to ask is when you're changing your daughter's nappy when she wakes in the morning or after her nap. She should be feeling refreshed and happy at these times.

There's a good chance that she'll feel a bit anxious and say no, in which case leave it for a day or so. This isn't a race and it's important that your little girl doesn't feel pushed into potty training. You can always ask again at bath time when your daughter won't be wearing her nappy.

It doesn't matter what time of day you pick to have a potty-training session, although we suggest that you avoid choosing a time because she's due to have a poo. If your daughter poos at roughly the same time each day it can be tempting to time a potty-training session around this. However, there will be too much anticipation and she'll sense the pressure. The key to our method is to stay relaxed.

Get her Ready

When your daughter says yes, and so gives her 'permission' to begin, help her to choose her knickers and to put them on. Try to avoid tights and trousers because these will make getting to the potty on time more difficult. Also, your little girl will feel more 'bundled up' so will be more likely to forget that she isn't wearing a nappy. You can put on a pair of socks to keep her warm.

Once she's dressed in her knickers, show her where the potty is and put her star chart up. You can also give her a drink – she'll need to wee about 20 minutes after drinking it.

DURING THE SESSION

Sitting on the Potty

At the start of the session, suggest that your daughter has a go at sitting on the potty and explain that she has to pull her knickers down. Chances are she won't need to go the first time, but give her lots of praise anyway. Tell her she's a clever girl just for sitting.

Don't make her sit on the potty for too long – 30 seconds is enough or she'll become uncomfortable and bored. Some training methods suggest sitting a child on the potty in front of a DVD, but we don't recommend this. Our method is about helping the child herself to become aware that she needs to go, rather than randomly catching her wees and poos because she spends so long sitting on the potty.

Wait

Once your daughter has had a go at sitting on her potty, there's little to do apart from wait and see if she happens to need a wee or poo in the next hour or so. In the meantime, play together and keep an eye out for signs that your little girl needs a wee – she may hold herself or wriggle from side to side. Some little girls will want to hide away if they need a poo, or will stop playing and look a bit worried.

If you suspect that she needs to go then suggest that she sits on the potty again. Try not to ask her to sit on the potty more than once every 30 minutes because she'll find it irritating. After all, she's having one-to-one playtime with Mummy so won't want this interrupted too often.

Stars

Ensure that your daughter gets at least one sticker per potty-training session – even for putting her knickers on or sitting on her potty. This will help her associate potty training with success. It's important not to make her feel like a failure, even if she doesn't pick it up quickly.

Her First Accident

If her first wee or poo is on the floor, don't allow her to feel like a failure. Say, 'Ooh, you've done a wee and it's made a puddle on the floor because you're not wearing a ...' and let her fill in the word 'nappy'. Say, 'You're such a big girl that next time you can wee in the potty,' and so on.

If she has a wee accident, wipe her then change her knickers into 'nice fresh ones', then you can clean up the floor together. Be pleasant, but don't give praise or she'll get confused about where she's supposed to wee.

If she has a poo accident, clean her up with wipes as you would after a dirty nappy. Then dress her in clean knickers and put her soiled ones in a nappy bag to be dealt with later. Clean up the poo as quickly and with as little fuss as possible. Stay positive throughout – say, 'Ooh look, the poo has gone in your knickers because you weren't wearing a nappy and next time you can do a poo in the ...' and let her fill in the word potty.

Her First Success

The first time your daughter does a wee or poo in the potty, go crazy with the praise. Clap, kiss her, phone Daddy to tell him and award her a particularly pretty sticker. Give her your full attention and loads of praise for at least a few minutes, and she'll soon be on that potty again. The idea is that she gets far more attention for a success than an accident.

Wiping

Explain that when she's wearing pants she has to wipe herself after using the potty. Then, when she does a wee or poo, wipe her from front to back 'just like Mummy'. Don't let her wipe herself just yet because this needs to be done carefully, particularly after a poo, to avoid her getting the bacterial infection vulvovaginitis (*see Chapter 9*). This is when bacteria are transferred from the anal region to the vagina and vulva.

Let your daughter become used to you wiping her over the next couple of days because she's going to need your help with wiping after a poo until she is about five or six, when she'll be able to competently wipe herself. And you'll need to help her wipe after a wee until she is about three when she'll have the manual dexterity to wipe herself.

You may need to teach your daughter to wipe herself after a poo when she starts nursery at three – she won't be very competent but on the few occasions when she's on her own, at least she'll be able to have a go.

If your daughter is fiercely independent and wants to do it herself, suggest that she tears the paper off the roll so that she feels involved – she'll find this quite difficult.

Over the coming days and weeks as your daughter learns to wee in her potty reliably, she can have a go at wiping after a wee. Show her how to hold the paper and wipe from front to back. A dabbing rather than a rubbing action is less likely to result in spreading bacteria.

AFTER THE SESSION

Nappy Back On

As soon as you put your daughter's nappy back on, there's a good chance that she'll do a wee or poo. This can seem quite irritating as you ask yourself why she couldn't have done this in the potty. However, it's actually a good sign and indicates that she has some control – she was simply feeling too anxious during the session to wee or poo and waited until she was securely back in her nappy again. This will change as your daughter gains confidence over the next few sessions. She will probably do a wee or poo in the potty within a couple of days because she is obviously aware enough to be able to hang on. All you can do is stay relaxed about where she wees or poos as this will take any pressure off and help her feel in control.

Cleaning Up

If your daughter managed to wee or poo in her potty then tip the contents down the loo and wipe the potty with antibacterial wipes. For a more thorough clean, you can also use an antibacterial spray, but do make sure you rinse this off carefully. To clean soiled knickers, use a wipe to scrape the worst of the poo into the toilet, then rinse the knickers in a bucket before putting them in the washing machine.

Check the Star Chart

Count how many stickers or stars your daughter has earned today. Praise her even if it's just one. Tell her that she can show Daddy when he comes home, and talk about how she can earn even more stars next time – by doing a wee in the potty perhaps.

Should You Proceed?

After your little girl's first potty-training session, you may feel that she simply isn't ready to come out of nappies yet. The following will help you decide whether to continue (in which case turn to Chapter 5), or whether to postpone potty training for a few weeks. If you decide to postpone it, simply don't mention potty training to your daughter for a little while – there's no need to make a big deal about it.

She Wouldn't Put her Knickers on

Don't insist that your little girl wears her knickers if she seems to be objecting. This may be her way of telling you that she's not ready to come out of nappies. Before you postpone potty training, try the following:

- Try her with nothing on her bottom half – it may take your daughter a week or so to come round to the idea of wearing pants.
- Buy some plainer knickers – sometimes little girls are worried about weeing or pooing in their very pretty knickers. Don't worry about wasting money on lots of different knickers – they'll get plenty of use over the coming months.

She Refused to Sit on her Potty

Again, this may be your daughter's way of saying she
wants to stay in nappies for a bit longer. Before you
postpone potty training, try asking if she'd like to sit on
a different potty. If her potty in the bathroom is pink
with stickers on it, and it's the one she's used to playing
with, then she may want to sit on this one rather than
the plainer potty you've given her for her potty session.
Try swapping the potties and you may have an instant
solution to the problem. (This is why we advised buying
two identical potties in Chapter 3.)

She Has Accidents

Of course children will have accidents during their early
potty-training sessions, but you have to work out why.
If your daughter was too busy playing to notice that she
needed the toilet then continue with the sessions. If,
however, she has no idea about when she's about to poo
or wee and seemed frustrated or bored during the
session, this suggests that she is still too immature to
come out of nappies.

Before you postpone potty training, try the following:

- Think back over the last few weeks and see if you
  can remember your daughter ever announcing that

she needed a wee or poo. This is a good indicator of whether or not she is mature enough for potty training.

- Try having a potty-training session at a different time of day – perhaps when your little girl is less tired or hungry as these factors can make children irritable and unable to concentrate and learn.

In an ideal world, everyone who reads this book will sail through D-day and proceed to the next stage of our potty-training programme. We don't expect that to happen, though, and realise that plenty of little girls won't be ready yet. If your daughter is one of these, try to stay relaxed because it really makes no difference in the long term whether she learns to use a potty quickly or slowly.

5

The Next Two Weeks

f D-day went well and your daughter seemed to enjoy her potty-training session then here's how to progress. Have as many or as few sessions in a day as you like – just do what fits around your schedule and family. Keeping things relaxed in this way will accelerate your daughter's learning. Don't be tempted to cram in too many sessions to try to push your daughter along because this will take the fun out of it. We suggest a maximum of three sessions a day for the first week, gradually extending the time that the nappy stays off. Don't worry if you happen to miss a day or two. It really doesn't matter; you can just carry on where you left off. The beauty of this training programme is that it is very flexible.

The following timetable is a rough estimate. All little girls are different and your daughter may progress faster or slower. It's not a race and it really doesn't matter whether it takes your daughter two days or over two months to get the hang of potty training. The important thing is that it remains fun and that you follow your daughter's lead. So only move on to the next stage when you're sure she's ready, not when you think she should be ready.

DAYS TWO AND THREE

Continue with the potty sessions, reminding your daughter to sit on the potty every 30 minutes or so. Give her lots of praise and stickers. If things seem to be going well and your little girl is enjoying the sessions, feel free to fit in up to three sessions a day, depending on your schedule. You can also lengthen the sessions to a couple of hours or more without a nappy – this will increase the chances of your little girl actually needing to go to the toilet during a session.

What You Can Expect

The first few sessions will result in accidents and the occasional wee or poo in the potty – usually after you've reminded your daughter to go. You'll notice that she soon becomes more confident about sitting on her potty and wees in it more frequently, perhaps even doing a poo.

What you're ultimately hoping for is that she will

actually tell you that she needs to do a wee or poo. This is a big milestone because it shows awareness of her bladder or bowel, plus the ability to hold on just about long enough to get to the potty (she'll only be able to hold for a few seconds at first but this will increase over the next few weeks as she matures). She may only ask for the potty once or twice during the early sessions, but this will increase with time.

How You Can Help

When your daughter asks for the potty, make a tremendous fuss, perhaps rewarding her with a particularly pretty sticker for her chart. If she's slower to ask for the potty and needs lots of reminding, stay calm. Remember that if she's done it once then she's got the physical capability and her brain is receiving signals that she needs to go, so she is bound to ask for the potty again quite soon.

If she doesn't ask for the potty at all during the first couple of days, don't worry. Just give her longer before moving on to the next stage, and remind yourself that the best way you can help is by allowing her to progress at her own pace. In the meantime continue to give her lots of encouragement, with a sticker every time she sits on the potty, wees or poos in it or washes her hands.

DAYS FOUR TO SEVEN – USING THE TOILET

Once your little girl has hit the big milestone of being able to ask for the potty, you can show her how to sit on the toilet. Note that she still won't be asking for her potty every time she needs a wee or poo, so do keep reminding her (although you won't be reminding her as often now).

What You Can Expect

Most little girls are willing to try sitting on the toilet but may take a couple of days longer to actually do a wee or poo. Eventually, your little girl should be as confident about weeing and pooing in the toilet as she is in her potty. Soon she'll hardly bother with her potty.

How You Can Help

Suggest that your daughter has a go at sitting on the toilet at bath time (she won't be wearing clothes and you'll both be near the loo so no last-minute dashes). If she refuses to sit on the toilet then respect her decision and simply repeat the suggestion in a couple of days. As long as you stay relaxed, she'll soon give it a go.

Give your daughter masses of praise for simply sitting on the toilet, even if she doesn't go – the toilet can seem very big to small children, and the flushing can be a bit scary. When she does finally wee or poo in the toilet give plenty of praise and stickers.

Continue to allow your daughter to wee in the potty if she wants to because she will have come to associate it with getting lots of praise. Be prepared, too, for her to have days when she doesn't feel up to the challenge of using the toilet. Never give your daughter the message that there's anything wrong with using the potty. In fact, travel potties can be invaluable when you're out and about and there are no nearby toilets (*see page 75*).

Garden Practice

If you've got a garden then encourage your little girl to squat down and wee in it because this will be an immense help when you're out. Small children have small bladders so can't hang on long, so if you're not near a toilet you may have to take emergency measures. If your daughter is comfortable with weeing behind a tree this will sometimes save her having an accident. So teach her to wee in the great outdoors – a skill she will occasionally resort to right into adulthood!

WEEK TWO – MORE PRACTICE AT HOME

Continue the sessions and using the toilet at home until your daughter rarely wears a nappy during the day and is able to tell you more than 50 per cent of the time that she needs the toilet. Children still need a bit of reminding for weeks, and sometimes months, after they're 'potty trained'. The aim is to build your daughter's confidence before you venture out so that you can minimise accidents outside the home.

What You Can Expect

Your daughter will soon become more or less toilet trained at home. She may even take herself off to the toilet, although this usually takes a few weeks longer. You can expect her to have the occasional accident for a couple of months. Don't worry – just react as normal in a calm, reassuring way.

How You Can Help

It's essential that you remain relaxed and avoid putting pressure on your daughter. Just give her lots of encouragement and watch her confidence grow.

TROUBLESHOOTING

She Willingly Sits on the Potty but Seems Unable to Wee

Lots of little girls sit on the potty but don't seem able to wee. This is because they aren't yet physically mature enough to know when they need to wee. If this is the case, you need to give your daughter another month or so to mature, so stop the potty sessions for now. Don't make a big deal about stopping the sessions because you don't want your little girl to feel like a failure.

If your daughter is particularly big or tall for her age, she may feel hunched up and uncomfortable on the potty. You could try moving straight to the toilet, but do use a child's toilet seat so that she feels secure.

She Becomes Tearful Every Time She Has an Accident

Some girls hate 'spoiling' their pretty knickers. Explain to her how easy it is to clean her knickers – she can help put the knickers in the washing machine and switch it on. Perhaps she could try not wearing any knickers for a few days while she builds confidence in weeing and pooing in her potty. It's important to give masses of reassurance about accidents and to tell your daughter that even Mummy and Daddy (and any other adults she admires) had accidents when they were little.

She Refuses to Sit on the Toilet

Little girls tend to be quite brave compared with boys, so your daughter will probably be willing to sit on the toilet. If she is hesitant then help to build her confidence by allowing her to flush away the wee and poo from her potty. Once you've tipped it down the loo, 'reward' her by letting her climb on to the closed seat so that she can flush the toilet as a special treat. Without realising, she'll come to associate getting on the toilet as a treat rather than something scary.

It's important not to pressurise her into sitting on the toilet. This has to be done in her own time – all you can do is casually suggest she gives it a try. Ensure that you've got a child's loo seat installed plus a stepping stool as both of these help children cope with the large size of a toilet.

She Won't Put her Nappy on to Go out

If your daughter is reluctant to wear a nappy when you're going out, by all means allow her to go nappy-less if you think she'll probably be okay (*see Chapter 6* for more on coping when you're out and about). Children sometimes know their own capabilities better than their parents. However, if you're pretty sure it will end in tears because she's not ready, persuade your daughter to wear a pull-up nappy – 'grown-up travel knickers'. Pull-ups are also useful for long car journeys, and your daughter can always change into her knickers on arrival. Alternatively, you could use a travel changing mat to protect her car seat – tell your daughter it's a travel mat to make her more comfortable.

If she's adamant that she wants to wear her knickers and refuses even to wear a pull-up, let her have her way. There's nothing to be gained by letting this become a battle. Be especially kind if she has an accident and resist saying 'I told you so', however tempting, as you struggle to clean her up in public.

By the end of this chapter your daughter will no longer wear a nappy at home and will be comfortable about using the potty and toilet. If she needs more time, that's fine. All children are different and it's important that she's happy about leaving her nappy off before you move on to the next stage, which is going out without a nappy on.

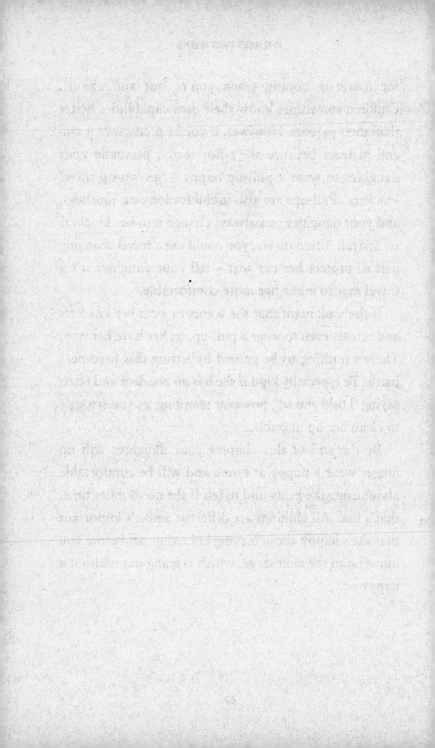

Out and About

After a couple of weeks you can think about taking your daughter out without her nappy on. Although potty training girls is usually easier than boys, when it comes to going out it can be a bit more challenging because they can't easily wee against the nearest tree or down a drain. It's therefore important to be sure that your daughter is physically capable of 'hanging on' before she wees. You can do this by not rushing to the toilet when you are at home – take your time and see if she is able to wait.

Another tip is to try teaching your daughter to sit on your toilet at home without her child's toilet seat. This can be very useful for using public toilets. Some children (especially those who are tall or agile) will be happy to do this. Whenever your daughter sits on an adult-sized toilet seat, do hold her firmly so that she feels secure and doesn't worry about slipping down the toilet.

If your little girl seems apprehensive about the 'big seat', don't push it – just buy a fold-up children's loo seat (*see Chapter 3*). These fit easily on to public toilet seats to make them smaller and easier for your daughter to sit on. Let your daughter practise with it at home so that it's familiar. It's also worth investing in a travel potty (*see Chapter 3*). Again, let your daughter have a go at using this before venturing out. There's a chance that you'll never have to use it, but it will give peace of mind during those early trips out.

CHECKLIST

The Going-out Checklist

☐ She doesn't wear a nappy at home during the day

☐ She usually tells you when she needs a wee or a poo

☐ She can 'hang on' a couple of minutes before doing a wee or a poo

☐ She is confident about sitting on a toilet (or a fold-up loo seat)

☐ She's happy to use a travel potty

Once you've ticked all of the above, you can take your daughter out and be reasonably confident that she will remain dry. There are bound to be some accidents over the next few weeks so pack spare knickers and tights, wipes and a plastic bag to put soiled clothes into. We also suggest protecting the buggy with a travel changing mat for the first week or so – mainly to minimise your stress and keep things nice and relaxed.

YOUR FIRST TRIPS OUT

Your first outing could be to the supermarket, a local café or a (tolerant) friend's house. Don't go too far from home in the first week – a day trip in the car is obviously more likely to result in accidents.

Tell your daughter where the toilet is when you arrive and ask if she needs to go. Chances are that she won't even go to the toilet on her first few trips out, especially if you keep them short. This stage is about confidence building, so when you get home, do tell your daughter how clever she is to have gone out without her nappy.

It's worth reminding little girls to go to the toilet whenever you happen to be near one. This will reduce the number of tedious public toilet searches. Get into the habit of asking if your daughter needs a wee before you leave home, and whenever you arrive somewhere with a toilet. She may be wary of using an unknown toilet, so tell her you need to go and suggest she comes along too. It's worth finding out where the toilet is in your local supermarket, library or anywhere else you may visit in the early weeks because when your daughter needs a wee you won't have long to get her there.

Public Toilets

Take wipes to wipe the seat, and some tissues in case there's no toilet paper. Also pack antibacterial hand gel in case there's no soap to wash hands afterwards. Some public toilets are particularly dirty, which can be tricky for little girls because they aren't tall enough to 'squat' over the seat. Wipe the seat before lifting her onto it then hold her securely. Your daughter is bound to touch the seat, and perhaps the floor when she bends over to be wiped. Try not to express any disgust as this will make her feel anxious; just use lots of wipes and anti-bacterial hand gel.

You can buy disposable paper toilet-seat covers which work out at about 10 pence each. We don't recommend them, though, because they slip and your daughter may not feel secure sitting on them. It's also important that she doesn't grow up being too fastidious about public toilets – we all need to use them and there's no point being too uptight about them.

Contrary to popular belief, you can't actually 'catch' anything from toilet seats. The only real risk is if your daughter touches the seat, gets some infected poo on her hands and transfers the germs via her mouth, which could give her a tummy bug and diarrhoea. This can be avoided with good hand washing.

Nowhere Near a Toilet

There will be times when your daughter announces she needs a wee or poo and there's just no way that you can get her to a toilet in time. You have a few options:

1. Squat

You may be able to find a quiet spot, perhaps behind a parked car, where you can help her squat. If you're in the country or a park, then she might be able to squat behind a tree. She will probably get wee over her knickers and tights, but don't worry too much – urine is sterile and will soon dry off. Some mums hold their daughters over drains as this is less messy but it's also back-breaking and not recommended.

2. Use the Travel Potty

This is a good option if you've got it with you, especially if your daughter needs a poo.

3. Put a Nappy on

It's worth keeping an emergency nappy in your handbag in the early days because you can put this on your daughter whenever she needs a wee or poo. This is a good solution when you're on public transport with no toilets because a portable potty could spill. Explain that it's just an emergency nappy and that she can take it off again as soon as you are able to clean her up.

Public Accidents

Some little girls are quite self-conscious about wetting themselves, and will be even more distraught if they soil their knickers. Make sure, therefore, that you are organised with a clean-up kit (wipes, nappy bag, clean knickers and tights) so you can sort your daughter out quickly and efficiently, minimising her embarrassment.

Ideally, take her into a baby change area or a disabled toilet where you can stuff her soiled clothes into a plastic bag, clean her up with wipes and give her clean knickers and tights (or trousers). If there's nowhere available, and not even a public toilet nearby, then find a quiet corner and change her out of wet clothes as quickly as possible to avoid fuss and embarrassment. Don't worry about wiping away wee because, as a one-off, being a bit damp won't do her any harm.

If she's soiled her knickers it can be trickier to sort her out, but again try to find a quiet corner and peel off dirty clothes carefully, sealing them in a plastic bag. Use wipes to clean up the worst of the poo – there's no need to do a perfect job in an emergency because you can do a thorough clean-up at home. Just change her into clean clothes.

Never get cross with your daughter for having accidents because she'll find this upsetting. She may even recognise it as a new device to get Mummy's attention, in which case you can expect more public accidents in future. Keep your manner low-key but pleasant: 'Oops, you've done a poo in your knickers. Next time we can find a grown-ups' toilet and you can get a special star.'

Dads – Taking Your Daughter to the Gents

When out, dads are often very embarrassed about taking their daughters to the loo but there may be emergency situations when they simply have to. The first hurdle is finding a toilet. A disabled toilet is generally the best option. If there isn't one available, you'll have to take her to the 'gents', in which case carry her straight into the cubicle to avoid her becoming curious and wandering off. Don't worry about the other men at the urinals – some will be dads and full of admiration, others will feel pity, and the majority won't even notice you.

Once inside the cubicle, give the seat a wipe with an antibacterial wipe (use toilet paper if you don't have wipes with you). Be quick because your little girl won't be able to hang on for long. Help your daughter on to the toilet (the disabled toilets are usually quite high up). Use a portable toilet seat if you have one, and offer to help hold your little girl on the toilet – she'll know what she wants.

When it comes to wiping, your daughter will probably be able to wipe herself after a wee, so just make sure she has a couple of sheets of toilet paper. Don't worry too much if she doesn't do a particularly good job – it's only wee. If she does a poo it's a different story as your daughter may still struggle with this. You'll need to wipe her from front to back to avoid infection. Make sure that you both wash your hands thoroughly afterwards.

THE NEXT FEW WEEKS

Once your daughter has become used to leaving home without her nappy, she's as good as potty trained. She'll become used to using public toilets when necessary, and to having a wee before leaving home. As she matures, she'll also find that she can 'hang on' for longer.

There will be occasional accidents – it's very common for three-year-olds to continue to have accidents every now and again – but you'll find that your daughter gradually becomes confident about taking herself off to the toilet unannounced at home, only asking for help with wiping after a poo. Accidents will become such a rarity that you'll soon start leaving the travel potty and eventually the change of clothes at home.

Encourage your little girl to use the toilet without her child's toilet seat because this will make going out much easier – you can always reintroduce the star chart as an extra incentive.

7

When Your Daughter Doesn't Fit the Mould

It's all very well giving a week-by-week guide to potty training your daughter, but little girls are all different and some simply won't comply. If this applies to your daughter, the following extra strategies will enable you to customise our potty-training method so that it works for her.

THE REBEL

Girls are naturally quite savvy and some will work out that accidents equal attention. Plenty of little girls have resorted to pooing and weeing for attention. This is particularly common when a new sibling arrives, leaving your daughter feeling very put out. It can also occur if there are other family stresses and your little girl isn't getting as much attention as she's used to.

Although it's shocking and disgusting to see your little princess deliberately pooing in her knickers like an angry convict, try to understand that she's still a baby herself and desperate for Mummy's love and attention. Your daughter is especially likely to 'protest' while you're breastfeeding the new baby because your attention will be instantly diverted from the baby to her – even if it is angry attention. As far as she's concerned, attention is attention and it makes no difference if it's angry attention.

Be reassured by the fact that protest pooing is normal and doesn't mean your daughter is deeply disturbed. It's easily dealt with by minimising your response. This is easier said than done, but do resist the temptation to freak out and yell because this will pretty much guarantee that your little girl repeats her performance. Pop your baby in his cot and clean your daughter up quickly and calmly without being chatty, using plenty of wipes and shoving dirty clothes in a bag to be dealt with later. Only start chatting and giving attention again to your little girl once you are settled back and feeding the baby.

Bear in mind that you were probably cooing over your newborn adoringly while your daughter watched unnoticed. Try giving your daughter a special dose of Mummy attention while you are breastfeeding by singing, telling stories or even watching children's television together. You could also try talking to her about her feelings – ask if she finds it difficult seeing you cuddling the baby because she wants a cuddle herself. Explain that babies take up a lot of time, but once the baby is asleep then you can have a lovely cuddle together. If she doesn't want to talk, just leave it. Your little girl will probably try protest pooing a few more times. Keep spare clothes and wipes to hand so that you can clean up really efficiently. If you keep your reaction consistent she'll soon give up.

Protest pooing can sometimes occur when parents are particularly 'nice' about cleaning up accidents. By all means give yourself a pat on the back for remaining calm when there's poo smeared around your home, but be careful that you don't inadvertently give your daughter a huge dose of kindly attention. We're not suggesting that you should get annoyed, but try to keep your response more neutral – aim to be calm and efficient rather than calm and kindly. When the mess is cleaned up, don't say much about it but switch to doing something completely different and only then give your little girl lots of chatty attention.

THE ENTHUSIAST

Some little girls are desperate to come out of nappies and wear pretty knickers like their older sister, cousins or friends. Although they are mentally ready, they are still very young and probably don't yet have the physical capabilities. The best way to deal with this is to give potty training a try to avoid this becoming a battle. Explain to your daughter that she can go without her nappy for a morning to see how she gets on. Do give her lots of praise for sitting on the potty, pulling her knickers up and down and so on, even if she proves incapable of knowing when she's about to wee or poo. After her session, give her lots of praise and tell her that she can have another go at using the potty another day – hopefully she'll forget about it for a little while before wanting another go.

In the meantime you could let her have her own 'knicker drawer' so the concept of growing up will still seem within her grasp. She'll probably enjoy taking her knickers out and admiring them, perhaps trying them on dolls.

THE ARTIST

If your daughter loves painting and colouring in, you may find that she becomes so absorbed in her drawings and has such excellent concentration that she sometimes wets herself. Becoming very involved in play is probably one of the most common reasons for girls to have accidents.

The problem will naturally resolve itself as the signals to go to the toilet become stronger with age, and also as her bladder develops, allowing her to 'hold on' for long enough to finish her picture. In the meantime you can suggest that your daughter goes to the toilet before her colouring, and don't make too much fuss when she has an accident. Just explain that she was concentrating so hard that her body didn't notice that it needed a wee – keep positive so that your little girl doesn't become self-conscious and worried about having accidents.

THE CHILD WHO DOESN'T MIND WET KNICKERS

Most little girls are fastidious about hygiene and won't stand for being in wet knickers. As a result, they will tell you the moment they have wet themselves and be eager to change into clean clothes. Because they don't like being wet they will be motivated to learn to use the potty quickly. Not all little girls are like this, however, and some really won't care about being wet.

If your daughter is quite laid back and happy to play for hours wearing wet knickers (a characteristic more often seen in little boys), do check her knickers and tights regularly to see if she's had an accident. She may end up a bit sore if she's wet for a long time. When you do discover that she's wet but hasn't told you, don't make a big deal about it. Just say, 'Oh, you've done a wee. Let's get you into nice fresh clothes.'

Don't give her extra attention – positive or negative. Remind yourself that she's not deliberately weeing in her knickers; she's still very young and simply learning. Okay, it may take her a little longer to learn than if she were more aware of being wet and soggy, but she'll get there before long and the day will come when she's dry all the time. In the meantime you can console yourself with the fact that she's not a fusspot.

THE CONTORTIONIST

Little girls with older brothers may insist on weeing standing up. If they push their tummies out, it's just about possible for girls to wee into the toilet while standing or against a tree, although it will probably be a bit messy. Watching your daughter standing to wee will seem a bit strange but she isn't weird, and it doesn't mean she'll grow up to be butch – she's just copying her brothers so don't make a big deal about it. You'll probably find that she grows out of it as soon as she starts nursery and sees other little girls weeing (at nursery, the toilet doors are usually very short and don't lock, and lots of children happily go to the toilet in full view of each other).

THE FALSE-ALARM CHILD

You've just got to the front of the queue at the bank and your little girl announces, 'Mummy, I need a poo.' Your obvious reply is, 'Can you wait a couple of minutes?' To which her obvious response is, 'No, it's coming now.' So you lose your place in the queue, curse as you realise you'll have to come back to the bank another time, then race off to find the nearest toilet. When you get there, your daughter sits down then calmly explains that she doesn't need to go any more.

Many parents would lose their temper at this point but that really isn't the answer. False alarms are quite common when children are toilet training, and your daughter may get genuinely confused from time to time about whether she needs the toilet or not. Also, the stress of rushing to find a toilet can sometimes stop her needing to go. If you react, this can easily become a great new device for getting your attention; or worse, it could make your daughter feel anxious about asking for the toilet next time. So bite your tongue, resist getting annoyed and simply say, 'Oh well. You can always try again later.' False alarms may go on for a few weeks and can be very tedious. Resist showing you're annoyed in any way and the problem will resolve itself.

THE LATE STARTER

Although lots of little girls have the physical ability to control their urine and bowel movements soon after their second birthday or earlier, there are plenty of exceptions. Don't push your daughter if she's a late starter because the pressure will make her feel anxious, especially when she clearly lacks the physical capability to progress. If you push her too soon, she'll probably fail and you'll have to restart potty training in a few months, dragging out the whole process.

Girls who are late starters are quite unusual as it tends to be boys who are the slow ones to come out of nappies. You're bound to know other little girls of her age or younger who are already potty trained. You have to do what is right for your daughter, though, and in this case it is to be patient and only proceed with potty training when she's showing the signs of being physically ready (*see Chapter 1*). There's also a chance that she's late to become mentally ready – again, unusual for girls but it happens. You must wait until she is showing the signs that she has the mental maturity before proceeding (*see Chapter 1*).

If your daughter is one of the slower ones to come out of nappies, it's important to abandon any preconceived ideas you may have had about getting her potty trained by a certain age. Instead, remind yourself that she will get there in the end. If she's six months behind her friends or cousins, so what? If you don't care, she certainly won't. In the meantime, you'll probably get a few comments and 'helpful suggestions' from well-meaning friends and relatives. Don't give in to their pressure. Be confident that you are doing what is right for your little girl – after all, you know her best. Explain to 'helpful' friends that your daughter isn't yet showing the signs that she's ready to come out of nappies; and when she is ready, you'll perhaps try out some of their suggestions. Grandmothers can be trickier because they are from a generation that tried to get children out of nappies as early as possible, driven by the fact that they may have used cloth nappies and possibly didn't have a washing machine. Reassure them that you are intending to start potty training your daughter within the next few months or so, but you are watching for signs that she has the physical capability. If all else fails and they keep going on, you could show them this book!

If your daughter ever starts asking why other girls wear knickers rather than nappies, simply use this as a cue to give potty training a go. If it turns out that she still isn't physically ready, see 'The Enthusiast' (*page 85*) for tips on persuading her to wait.

How to Resume Potty Training after a Failed Attempt

If your daughter has reached the age of three and is showing no willingness to use the potty, it's probably because you tried to train her before she was mature enough, or at a difficult time such as the arrival of a new baby, and she's come to associate potties with stress. She won't be the only one. You too will dread getting the potty out because you know it ends in accidents and tears.

You can resolve this. Although your daughter is old enough to be physically ready to come out of nappies, you need to help her to become mentally ready too because at the moment there's a bit of a block. Put her back in nappies for six weeks and don't mention potties or knickers unless your daughter does first.

After six weeks, ask your little girl if she'd like to have another go at using the potty. She will probably say no because she's testing you and making sure that the pressure really is off. So let her have her way and say,

'Okay, maybe another day.' Resist mentioning potties for another week then ask her again. Don't appear anxious or in any way bothered that she's not interested, and she'll probably agree after a couple more weeks. You can give her extra encouragement by showing her a packet of chocolate buttons and saying that she can earn these as well as stickers for every time she sits or does a wee on the potty. Although some parenting experts would frown about giving children sweets as 'bribes', plenty of mums will testify that it works. Once again, let your daughter be the one to decide whether today is the day.

When she finally agrees, she has effectively given her 'permission' to restart potty training so will be feeling in control and a lot less anxious than before. You will probably find that she learns very quickly. It's very unlikely that she won't ever agree because she'll be aware of other little girls her age using the potty or toilet and will eventually want to be like her peers.

8

Night Training

The first time your daughter goes to bed without wearing her nappy, you'll no doubt be bracing yourself to be woken in the small hours to change bedding and night clothes. Although bedwetting happens to pretty much all children from time to time, the upside is that girls generally have fewer problems with wetting the bed than boys and tend to go through the night earlier.

Girls often manage to stay dry at night around the time of their third birthday, a few months after they have been potty trained. Do remember, though, that all children are different and develop at varying rates. Some little girls will find it physically impossible to stay dry through the night until they are four or five. One in six five-year-olds regularly wets the bed, according to the Enuresis Resource and Information Centre. However, bedwetting is rarely anything to worry about (*see Chapter 9* to rule out any underlying medical problems). You can take comfort from the fact that health professionals don't even recognise bedwetting as a problem until the age of six because it is so common among small children. You only need to seek help from your doctor if, after the age of six, your daughter is wetting the bed more than twice a week.

As a parent, it's important to take a relaxed approach and to reassure your daughter so that she doesn't become anxious about wetting the bed or having to wear a nappy at night. It's particularly difficult for girls who are late night-time developers because they will be different to most other girls their age. Try not to worry that there's anything wrong with your daughter, or even that it is your fault in some way. You just have to accept that there's nothing you can do to speed things along because it's all down to your daughter's physical development, and this is controlled entirely by nature, not nurture.

HOW THE BODY DEVELOPS TO STAY DRY AT NIGHT

It's impossible for your little girl to have night control until she is physically mature enough. This is what must happen:

- She needs to produce enough vasopressin. This anti-diuretic hormone suppresses urination at night by slowing the production of urine. It tends to kick in from around 18 months, although in some children it doesn't do so until the age of six.

- Her nervous system must be mature enough. This will enable it to trigger a strong signal during sleep telling her that her bladder is full and needs emptying. This signal needs to be strong enough to wake her, so must be stronger than the full-bladder signals she receives during the day. This is why children usually learn to be toilet trained during the day before they can go without nappies at night.
- Her bladder needs to be large enough. This will mean it can hold a large enough quantity of urine to avoid needing to get up throughout the night. Bladders grow rapidly from the age of two until four, explaining why lots of children come out of night nappies once they are three.

WHEN TO LEAVE THE NIGHT NAPPY OFF

Most little girls will be ready to go without their night nappy a few months after they manage to be dry during the day – often around her third birthday and usually before the age of four. Girls generally find night control easier than boys, and some will learn to stay dry during the night at the same time as they come out of daytime nappies. Try leaving the night-time nappy off while potty training if you think your daughter is physically ready. More than three wet beds in a week suggest that she's not yet physically mature enough and should go back to night nappies.

Early Signs that She May Be Ready to Try

- She remains dry during her nap. This is one of the first indicators that your daughter has some control over her bladder during sleep. Once she is potty trained, put a fresh nappy on for her nap and see if it's still dry when she wakes up. You can start leaving her nap-nappy off once she has had 10 consecutive dry naps.

- She is able to 'hold on' for a wee. This shows good bladder control. As your daughter matures you'll notice that she is able to hang on longer before she wees. Once she can wait several minutes you could try leaving her nappy off at night if she's keen to give it a try.

- She says she doesn't want to wear a nappy at night. Lots of little girls are desperate to be grown-up and will decide themselves when they are ready to abandon their night nappy. You may well find that she is indeed ready to stay dry at night but some girls overestimate their maturity and will end up wetting the bed. Give it a couple of weeks and use nappy mats and towels to save on laundry. If, however, she's having more than three accidents a week, you could gently suggest that she waits a few more weeks for her body to be ready. If she's reluctant, then try getting her into pull-ups (*see page 107*).

Definite Signs that She is Ready to Try

- She wakes up in the night to wee in the toilet or potty. This shows she is well and truly ready to leave her night nappies behind. Her brain's signals that she needs a wee are now so strong that they wake her up. Be aware that most children don't get up for a wee in the night if they are wearing a nappy.
- Her nappies are still dry in the morning. This is a sure sign that she no longer needs to wear a nappy at night. She now has enough of the hormone vasopressin, which suppresses night-time urination. If she has had several consecutive dry morning nappies, let her have a nappy-free night. Note that some children will wee in their nappy as soon as they wake up and won't go to the toilet until they are not wearing a nappy.

When your daughter shows at least one of the above signs and only has very occasional accidents during the day, you can try leaving her nappy off at night.

HOW TO COME OUT OF NIGHT NAPPIES

Get her Permission

Ask if she'd like to try leaving off her night nappy, and go ahead only if she seems keen. If there is any reluctance on her part, simply postpone the big night for a couple of weeks or until your daughter is happy about the idea. It's important that she doesn't feel pushed into leaving off her night nappy because she'll get particularly anxious should she have an accident. Also, feeling stressed can sometimes make children more likely to wet the bed.

Buy a Big Bed and a Night Light

It's essential that your little girl is out of her cot and in a big bed before she starts night training or she won't be able to get to a potty or toilet during the night. You can leave a potty by the bed (not ideal if the bedroom is carpeted), or leave the potty in the upstairs toilet. Some little girls will happily use the toilet in the night, especially if they have become used to using the toilet, rather than the potty, during the day.

Make sure that there is either a night light in your daughter's bedroom or a hall light on so that your daughter can easily find her way to the toilet or potty in the night. If she does get up in the night for a wee, encourage her back to bed quickly. Don't give too much praise in the middle of the night or she'll become fully awake and may even want to play.

Protect the Bed

Use a mattress cover under the sheet – the plastic ones get a bit sweaty so we suggest you use a cotton-quilted one (available from most shops that sell bedding). You can give extra protection by putting a disposable nappy mat (from chemists) or a towel under your daughter's bottom in the early weeks. These can be whipped out in the middle of the night, usually leaving the bed dry underneath.

Monitor her Drinking Pattern

Ensure that your little girl has plenty to drink during the day because dehydration can irritate the bladder, making her want to wee more frequently. Once you're sure that she's getting plenty to drink, you can stop giving her drinks in the hour before bedtime. It may take a few days to adjust your daughter's drinking pattern.

Remind her to Have a Wee before Bedtime

Get into the habit of reminding your daughter to have a wee before she goes to bed. If she's been in bed a while before lights out, ask if she needs a wee before going to sleep. Offer to help her get out of bed because she may be feeling too tired to bother otherwise.

Wake her for a Night Wee

Your daughter may sleep for up to 12 hours at night, which is a long time for anyone to go without having a wee. It may be worth getting her up for a wee during the first couple of months of night training to reduce her chances of wetting the bed. Make sure that you wake her up and that she doesn't 'wee in her sleep', which will lead to bad habits and make bedwetting more likely.

When you wake her, usually before you go to bed yourself, you may find that she takes ages to actually have a wee and sometimes doesn't seem to need one. Once you've helped her on to the potty or toilet, ask if she needs a wee – she may only be able to nod or shake her head as she'll be too tired to speak. Also, try turning on a tap as the sound of running water may help her to wee. You'll find that after a few nights she gets used to being woken up for a wee and will be able to perform a bit quicker. There will be occasions when she simply doesn't need to go, so do accept this and pop her back to bed even if she hasn't been. There's still a reasonable chance she'll stay dry until morning.

What to Do when She Wets the Bed

It's not a matter of *if* she wets the bed but *when*. Just about all children will wet the bed when they are learning to go through the night. This means having to wake up and change bed linen. Stay calm and never show any signs of irritation with your daughter. Keep a spare nightdress and sheet to hand so that you can sort your daughter out quickly. If you've put a towel or nappy mat down, you may find that the sheet is still dry underneath, which makes things very easy.

The Next Morning

Make a big fuss of your daughter if she managed to remain dry. If she did wet the bed, don't worry or get cross – it wasn't your daughter's fault and shows that she's not physically mature enough to stay dry every night. Never assume it was because she was too lazy to get out of bed to wee. Be patient, and kindly explain to your little girl that our bodies grow up at different rates and that hers is still changing so that one day she will find it easy not to wet the bed.

Should You Continue?

When your little girl starts night training, do bear in mind that a few accidents are completely normal and to be expected. However, if she's having more than three accidents in a week, then her body probably isn't yet mature enough so put her back in nappies for a month or two. If she's staying dry most nights and only having one or two accidents a week persevere because in a couple more weeks she'll have even fewer wet nights. Should she get very upset by the accidents, you can always pop her back in night nappies to allow her time to mature a little more.

TROUBLESHOOTING

She Refuses to Wear a Nappy at Night

Lots of little girls are keen to be 'big girls' and will make a fuss about wearing a nappy at night even if they keep wetting the bed. Try persuading your daughter that pull-ups are 'big girl night nappies', or let her decorate a pull-up nappy with felt-tip pens and stickers during the day and call it 'princess night knickers'. Tell her she's only allowed to wear it at night, and come bedtime she will hopefully be keen to put it on.

It Seems Impossible for her to Learn to Stay Dry at Night

Plenty of little girls still need night nappies when they are four and may wet the bed occasionally even when they are five. Some will remain in night nappies until they are six. If your daughter is a late developer it's essential never to pressurise her but accept that her body simply isn't mature enough for her to stay dry at night. Just give her masses of reassurance and talk to her about bladder size and brain signals. Explain that once her body is ready she will find it easy to stay dry every night.

She's Been Invited to a Sleepover but She still Wets the Bed

Being a late developer is particularly hard for girls as they are more socially mature than boys and many start to have sleepovers from about the age of four or five. Sadly, there's no magic way to make her stay dry at night when she stays with friends, and she'll actually be more likely to wet the bed if she's anxious.

When she gets the sleepover invite, do ask her if she actually wants to go – she may decide that she doesn't because of the risk of wetting the bed. If she does want to go then mention her bedwetting to the other child's mother, and tell your daughter that she can tell the other mum if she does wet the bed.

We suggest buying night pants, which are pull-up nappies in pretty designs shaped to look more like knickers than a nappy. Available from chemists, they are disposable and your daughter could wear one under her nightdress. You can also buy incontinence briefs online. These don't look as nappy-like as the disposables and are basically briefs with a sewn-in absorbent pad. They are available in tiny sizes, from two to three years and upwards.

Just like potty training, night training can't be rushed. When it happens will be very much dictated by your daughter's physical development and all you can do in the meantime is gently guide her and be very patient.

9

Resolving Common Medical Problems

When children have trouble with potty training or bedwetting, you just have to wait patiently for them to mature and the problem will usually resolve itself. Occasionally, however, there is a medical condition at the root of your child's training troubles. If this is the case then you'll need to see your doctor. Here are some conditions to be aware of.

URINARY TRACT INFECTION (UTI)

This is 10 times more common among girls than boys because they have a much shorter urethra (tube that leads from the bladder to outside the body), which makes it easier for bacteria to enter the body. If your daughter suddenly starts to wet herself after being dry for a while, or she wets the bed more often, it may be due to an infection. This is because urinary tract infections cause more frequent weeing. Other symptoms to look out for include: doing a small amount of wee at a time; pain on urination; fishy-smelling urine; a fever; vomiting; and abdominal pain.

What You Can Do

Although anxiety can be the reason for bedwetting or more frequent accidents you should take your little girl to the doctor in case she has an infection. A simple urine test will show if there is an infection that needs to be treated with antibiotics. To help prevent re-infection, and to help stop your daughter getting a urinary tract infection in the first place, always wipe her from front to back. This reduces the chances of bacteria from the anus entering the vagina. Also, give her plenty to drink because a faster and more frequent flow of urine gives bacteria less time to multiply in the bladder.

VULVOVAGINITIS

Lots of little girls suffer from this when they come out of nappies. Gut bacteria (found in poo) are transferred from the anal region to the vagina and vulva, causing inflammation, soreness and itchiness. It's therefore important that little girls have help wiping thoroughly and from front to back.

Although baby girls can get covered in poo, they generally don't get vulvovaginitis because their nappies are changed quickly. Once out of nappies, though, if a little girl does a bad job of wiping herself after a poo she could remain a bit 'dirty' for hours on end until she has a bath or someone checks and wipes her properly – perhaps when she gets home from nursery or school. Also, once little girls are out of nappies they can scratch themselves, making the skin around the vagina and vulva more vulnerable to infection – and of course touching herself can transfer infection.

Vulvovaginitis isn't serious and doesn't affect girls after the age of about eight as the body prepares for puberty and starts to make oestrogen, which strengthens the vaginal skin.

What You Can Do

Your doctor may take a swab and prescribe antibiotics, antibacterial cream or oestrogen cream to help minimise any discomfort. You can take steps to try to avoid the condition in the first place and to manage it if your daughter does suffer because it can be quite uncomfortable. Whenever possible, then, help your daughter to wipe herself – especially after a poo – and always from front to back. If she's fiercely independent, let her have the first couple of wipes then say something like, 'You've done so well I bet Mummy can't wipe any more off.' Cotton knickers and avoiding bubble bath can also help reduce irritation, and do keep your daughter's nails short to minimise scratching the skin.

THRUSH

This is a fungal infection caused by *Candida albicans*, which thrives in warm damp conditions such as the vagina. As well as being sore and itchy, there is a thick white discharge. Thrush isn't a sexually transmitted disease – it's a common infection that can affect people of all ages. It's often seen after antibiotics for another condition such as tonsillitis or an ear infection.

What You Can Do

If you suspect your daughter may have thrush, seek medical help because this fungal infection is easily treated. Your doctor will probably prescribe an anti-fungal cream and you should see an improvement within a couple of days. It's important to continue the treatment after symptoms have disappeared to prevent a recurrence. Again, cotton knickers can help because the cooler your daughter is, the less prone she will be to infection.

DIABETES

Every year, more than 1,500 children in Britain develop diabetes mellitus – the amount of sugar in the blood is too high and the excess glucose is passed out of the body in the urine. If your daughter has diabetes, she will wee a lot more and be very thirsty, even getting up in the night for a drink. She may also seem generally lethargic and unwell, and sometimes children with diabetes will suddenly start having more accidents and wetting the bed.

What You Can Do

Get medical help because diabetes must be managed with insulin injections. You will also be told how to help balance your daughter's blood sugar levels by ensuring that she eats regularly and sticks to particular foods.

CONSTIPATION

D ry, hard poos and straining on the toilet are sure signs of constipation. Address this quickly because constipation can become painful and your daughter may start to withhold her poos and make the problem worse. It may even cause anal fissures (*see page 118*).

If you don't sort this condition out, your daughter could develop chronic constipation and overflow incontinence. This is when dry, hard stools become lodged in the back passage and any poo that manages to get past gets squashed, broken up and looks like diarrhoea. You may notice that her knickers are smeared with poo even if you're sure that her bottom is being wiped properly. Eventually, your daughter will start soiling her pants because the poo that is lodged in the rectum confuses the sensations in the bowel and she won't know when her bowel is full and she needs a poo. The final stage of chronic constipation is that she will become unable to tell when she needs a wee and start wetting herself.

What You Can Do

- See your doctor who will confirm constipation by feeling your daughter's tummy, and rule out any rare anatomical problems. Sometimes an X-ray is arranged to confirm this. Your doctor may prescribe laxatives and stool softeners.

- Stress can make constipation worse, so reassure your daughter that it's not her fault if she's been pooing in her knickers.

- Make sure that your daughter drinks plenty because dehydration can slow bowel movements.

- Gradually introduce more fibre into her diet by giving her more fruit, vegetables, dried fruit, beans, porridge and brown bread. It's important to increase her fibre intake very gradually because a sudden, large increase will probably cause wind, bloating, tummy ache and diarrhoea.

- If your daughter's poos have been dry, hard and painful she may have become anxious about going to the toilet. Make sure, though, that she doesn't hold on when she needs to go because poos can change from soft to hard in a few hours. Get her to the toilet quickly when she says she needs a poo and encourage her to go by reassuring her that pooing won't be so painful if she goes now rather than later, and if she drinks plenty and eats the fibrous food you give her. Explaining to your daughter what constipation is and how you are sorting it out will help her to feel less anxious.

ANAL FISSURE

A small tear in the anus can cause very painful pooing and also some bleeding (the bleeding is nothing to worry about once a fissure has been diagnosed). The cause of fissures is usually constipation – forcing out hard stools (*see page 116*). Your daughter will be reluctant to poo, particularly in the potty or toilet if she's only recently started potty training. If she's in pain, she'll opt instead for the familiarity of her nappy.

Straining can also cause anal fissures. A bit of pushing is fine but if your daughter is really struggling then suggest that she tries to do a poo a bit later instead (usually another five minutes or so). Straining can be a sign that she's a bit constipated so do watch her diet and fluid intake.

What You Can Do

See your GP because it's important to get a diagnosis, particularly if you spot any bleeding. Your GP may prescribe a soothing cream to put on your daughter's perianal region (the area around the anus). Healing can take a while because the skin in the anus is wet. A small dab of Vaseline to lubricate the anus just before your daughter does a poo can help alleviate discomfort.

Because anal fissures nearly always result from constipation it's essential to get this sorted out. Do follow all the tips on avoiding constipation (*above*) as this condition can make anal fissures particularly painful. The fissure won't be able to heal if your daughter remains constipated.

ADHD, AUTISM AND OTHER LEARNING DIFFICULTIES

Learning difficulties make potty training particularly challenging, and if your daughter is affected you'll need masses of patience. Don't attempt to get her out of nappies too soon because having a 'false start' would be very disruptive for her. You want to be sure that she is physically ready.

What You Can Do

Follow our method. This should work well as it aims to minimise the pressure put on the child. Be prepared for potty training to take longer than it takes other children. Ask your doctor or whoever helps you with your daughter's condition about getting some help with potty training. They may also give you some advice and tips that are relevant to teaching your daughter.

Frustrating Days

If your daughter's toilet training is delayed because of a medical condition then do be reassured that there is plenty of help available. On those frustrating days when you think she'll never succeed, just remind yourself that she will get there in the end – and what's a few extra months anyway?

Moving Forwards

When accidents are a rare occurrence and your daughter is confident about going to the toilet, we'd say that she was potty trained. Although this happens relatively painlessly for most little girls, some will take a while to reach this stage. If your daughter is one of the slower ones, it will sometimes feel as though she'll never be reliably dry, but she will get there – probably without you even noticing. You'll suddenly realise one day that your daughter hasn't wet herself for a while.

Whether your daughter was quick or slow to come out of nappies, over the coming weeks and months you'll see her becoming more independent – taking herself off to the toilet without even asking, and needing less and less help with wiping and hand washing. Her new skills will give her lots of confidence, and you and your daughter will feel proud as she makes this momentous step away from her baby years towards becoming a little girl. When she goes on play dates and starts school and nursery she'll be at a big advantage and will feel more confident about being away from you because she is fully toilet trained.

ACCIDENTS AND SETBACKS

Diarrhoea

Diarrhoea is common among toddlers, and if your daughter picks up an infection she is likely to soil her knickers. This doesn't mean that she's regressed; she's simply unwell. We suggest that you put her back in nappies for a day or so to save on mess. Be sensitive to your daughter and explain that a nappy would just be worn while she's ill and needs to rush to the toilet. Tell her it's difficult to get to the toilet in time, even for adults. If she's very reluctant to wear a nappy then don't force her – she's unlikely to have diarrhoea for more than about 24 hours.

Wetting the Bed

If your daughter is dry during the day but still wets the bed or even needs nappies at night, she is still, by our definition, 'potty trained'. Staying dry at night relies on your daughter being physically mature enough, which is all down to nature, so we always say that nights don't count.

Dealing with Accidents

Once your daughter has been dry for a while, don't worry if she suddenly has an accident. Most children wet themselves between the ages of three and four, and sometimes will even poo in their pants. Although common, it generally happens only a couple of times a month so your daughter is still 'potty trained'. Once again, it's simply a waiting game for parents as your daughter matures and slowly stops having any accidents at all.

When she does have an accident, she may feel as though she has failed because she will have come to associate using the toilet with lots of praise. Make light of it so that her confidence isn't knocked. Tell her that even big girls have accidents sometimes, and perhaps say, 'Never mind, these things happen. You must have been too busy concentrating on your colouring to remember to go to the toilet.'

Dealing with Setbacks

Sometimes your little girl will have more than just a random accident and will start wetting herself frequently, despite having been dry for months. Setbacks generally occur when she is stressed and can happen around the time of starting nursery, the arrival of a new sibling or perhaps moving house. Your daughter may start wetting herself in the run-up to these stressful events or once they have occurred. The best way to deal with a setback is not to deal with it. Make light of any accidents. Remember that accidents can also be a way of getting attention, which is another reason not to make too much fuss.

Some little girls will want to start using their potty again or even to wear a nappy. If this happens with your daughter, let her. She's only trying to be the much-loved baby so give her plenty of fuss and attention. She'll soon get fed up with soggy nappies and messy potties. Setbacks don't generally go on for more than a few weeks so keep your response to your little girl's regression low key and wait for it to pass.

We hope that you and your daughter have enjoyed our relaxed approach to potty training. We would like to leave you with some checkpoints to assess your daughter's progress.

Ten Signs that Your Daughter is Fully Potty Trained

1. You no longer even think about packing spare knickers and tights for her when you go out.

2. If she doesn't do a wee before she leaves home it's not a problem – you won't be searching for a toilet within the next 10 minutes.

3. Her pretty knickers are starting to look old and worn out.

4. The potty has become dusty and forgotten because she uses the toilet.

5. If you're going away for the night, you only pack one nightdress for her and don't bother taking a spare.

6. When you visit your local café you no longer glance over at the toilet to check there isn't an 'out of order' sign or a long queue.

7. When you go somewhere new you don't do an automatic check to see where the toilets are the minute you arrive.

8. She knows how to wipe from front to back and can wash her hands by herself.

9. You don't have to plan toilet stops on long car journeys – she goes when everyone else goes and there's never a wet car seat.

10. At home, your daughter trots off to the toilet by herself without even telling you.

Ticking three or more of these points shows that your daughter is well and truly toilet trained, so well done. If you can't tick the above points then your daughter isn't there yet so do keep up the encouragement and praise, and be patient. It will happen, we promise. In a couple of months or so, nappies and potties will start to become a distant memory, and when you hear other mums earnestly discussing the perils of toilet training, you'll wonder what on earth all the fuss is about.

Index

Pony Training Boys
the easy way

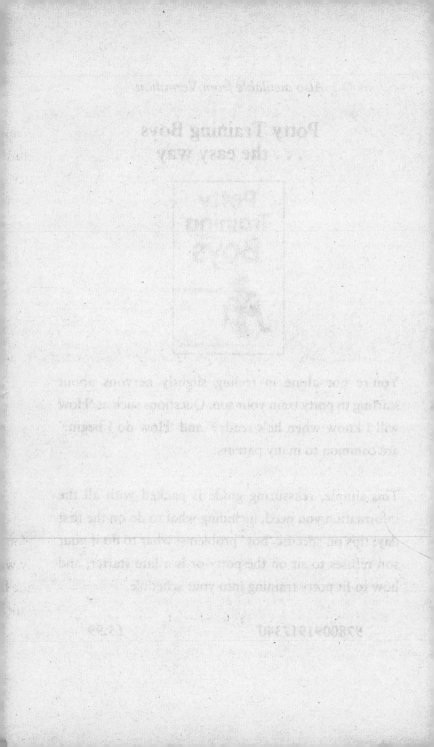

You're not alone in riding slightly nervous about starting in pony train veronica. Questions such as 'How will I know when he's ready?' and 'How do I begin?' are common to many parents.

This simple, reassuring guide is packed with all the information you need, including what to do on the test day; tips on specific 'boy' problems; what to do if your son refuses to sit on the pony - or is a late starter; and how to fit pony training into your schedule.

9780041513340   £3.99